Level

2

Opening Doors

Reading and Writing Activity Book

Linda Ventriglia, Ph.D.

Santillana USA
www.santillanausa.com

Santillana USAPublishing Company, Inc.
2105 NW86th Avenue
Miami, FL33122

The author gratefully acknowledges the editorial assistance of Jan Emiko Naguwa.

Opening Doors, Level 2
ISBN 10: 1-58105-836-5
ISBN 13: 978-1-58105-836-9

Production: Education Update, Inc.

Published in the United States of America.
10 09 08 07   15 16 17 18 19

Printed by HCI Printing and Publishing, Inc.

- Clap out the syllables in the characters' names.
- Write the character's name in the sentences.
- Read each sentence together.
- Finally, draw a picture of yourself. Then write your name.

 Sara

 Jason

What is your name?

My name is __Sara__.

What is your name?

My name is __Jason__.

 Maylee

 Lupita

What is your name?

My name is __Maylee__.

What is your name?

My name is __lupita__.

What is your name?

My name is __Shirley__.

ELD Standard
Answer simple questions with one- or two-word responses.
ELA Standard
Listen to and identify a sequence of sounds.

• Ask the questions: ***What's his name? What's her name?***
• Identify the beginning sound in the names.
• Circle the beginning letter of each name.

Sara

(S)   T   U

Pao

O   (P)   Q

Maylee

K   L   (M)

Carlos

B   (C)   D

Lupita

J   K   (L)

Jason

H   I   (J)

ELD Standard
Answer simple questions with one- or two-word responses.
ELA Standard
Identify alphabet letters.

Asking and Answering Questions

- Ask the questions around the group. *What's his name? What's her name?*
- Clap out the syllables in each name.

Sara

Her name is

<u>sara</u> .

Pao

His name is

<u>Pao</u> .

Maylee

Her name is

<u>Maylee</u> .

Carlos

His name is

<u>carlos</u> .

Lupita

Her name is

<u>Lupita</u> .

Jason

His name is

<u>Jason</u> .

ELD Standard
Answer simple questions with one- or two-word responses.
ELA Standard
Identify word parts by clapping out syllables.

- Write each character's name in the sentence.
- Ask a partner the questions: *What is his name? What is her name?*
- Clap out the syllables in each name.

Jason	**Sara**	**Pao**	**Maylee**	**Carlos**	**Lupita**

What is her name?

Her name is

Lupita.

What is his name?

His name is

Pao.

What is her name?

Her name is

Maylee.

What is his name?

His name is

Carlos.

What is her name?

Her name is

Sara.

What is his name?

His name is

Jason.

ELD Standard
Answer simple questions with one- or two-word responses. Use common social greetings.
ELA Standard
Listen to and identify parts of words by clapping out syllables.

4

- Identify the actions.
- Ask a partner the questions: *What is he doing? What is she doing?*
- Ask a partner to circle one action in each row.

standing

sitting down

jumping

walking

kneeling

hopping

turning around

smiling

jumping rope

swinging

crying

ELD Standard
Produce simple vocabulary to communicate basic needs in social and academic contexts.
ELA Standard
Follow one- and two-step oral directions.

TO THE TEACHER: Identify body parts.

- Point to one of the pictures in each row.
- Ask a partner the question: *What is this?*
- Draw a line under one of the body parts in each row.

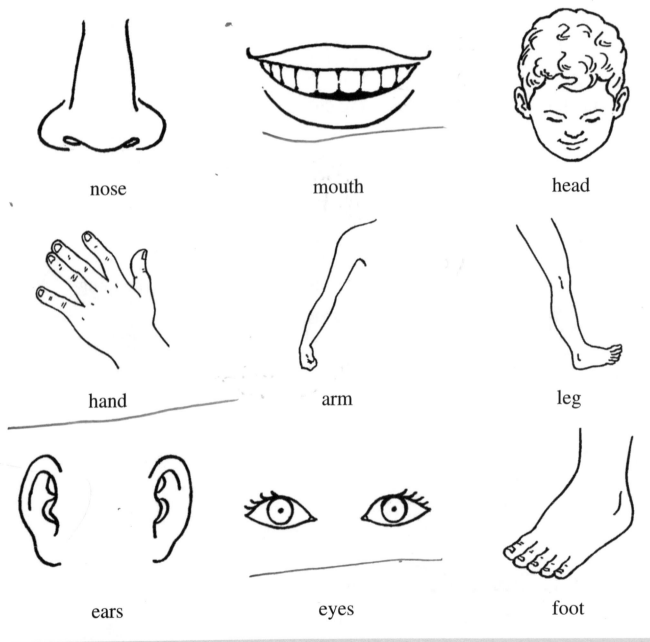

nose   mouth   head

hand   arm   leg

ears   eyes   foot

ELD Standard
Ask and answer questions using phrases or simple sentences.
ELA Standard
Match pictures with a verbal label.

> 🍎 **TO THE TEACHER:** Brainstorm with children strategies to help them create words that rhyme with "**face**" and "**nose**." For example, replace the letter "**f**" in "**face**" with other letters. start with "**a**" and work your way through the alphabet. Don't forget the consonant blends, such as "**pl**."

- Write words that rhyme with face and nose.
- Then cut and paste parts of the face together.
- Ask the "wh" questions: *What is this? What are these?*

face - race, place, _chace_ _space_ _base_

nose - hose, rose, _gose_ _toes_ _hose_

nose

ear   ear   mouth   eyes

ELD Standard
Ask and answer simple questions.
ELA Standard
Create and state a series of rhyming words.

7

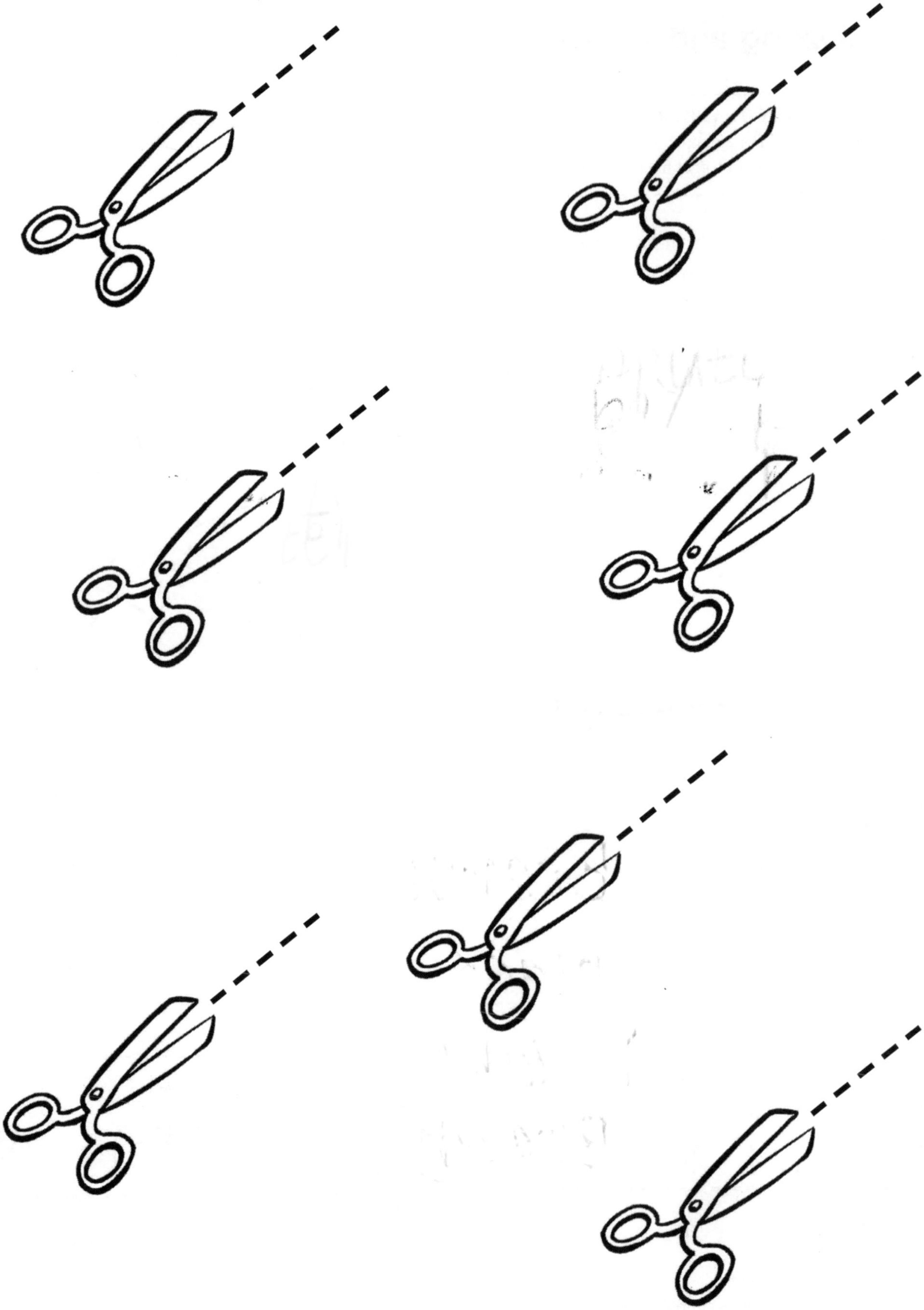

• Color the boy's and girl's hair and eyes.
• Then finish the sentences. Read the sentences to a partner.
• Ask a partner the question: *What color are his eyes?* or *What color are her eyes?*

The boy's hair is ___Brown___.

The boy's eyes are ___black___.

The girl's hair is ___Yellow___.

The girl's eyes are ___Brown___.

ELD Standard
Ask and answer simple questions.
ELA Standard
Respond to "*Who, What, When, Where,*" and "*How*" questions.

- Identify curly or straight hair.
- Write the word **curly** or **straight** under each picture.
- Ask a partner the question: *Is their hair curly or straight?*

curly

straight

curly

straight

curly

straight

ELD Standard
Ask and answer simple questions.

ELA Standard
Respond to "*Who, What, When, Where,*" and "*How*" questions.

10

Asking and Answering Questions

- Identify the clothing.
- Write the correct word under each picture. Read the words to a partner.
- Ask a partner the question: ***What is this?***

dress **shirt** **coat** **skirt** **sweater** **cap**

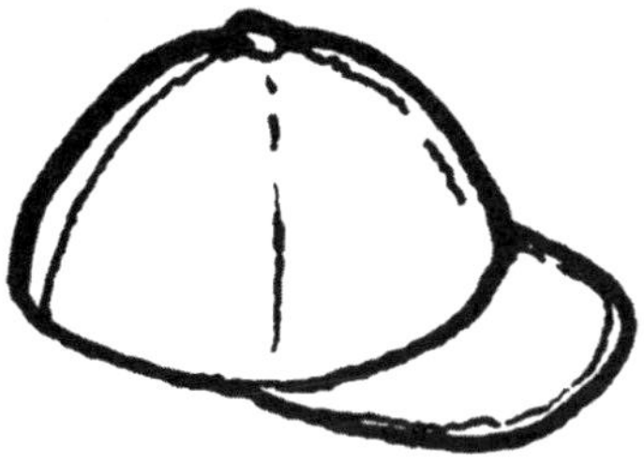

cap

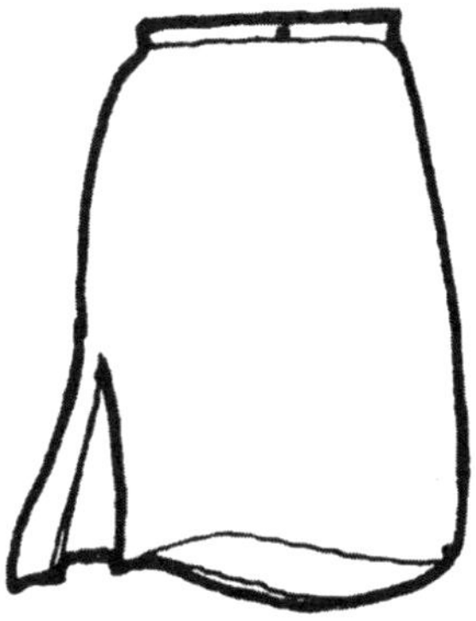

skirt

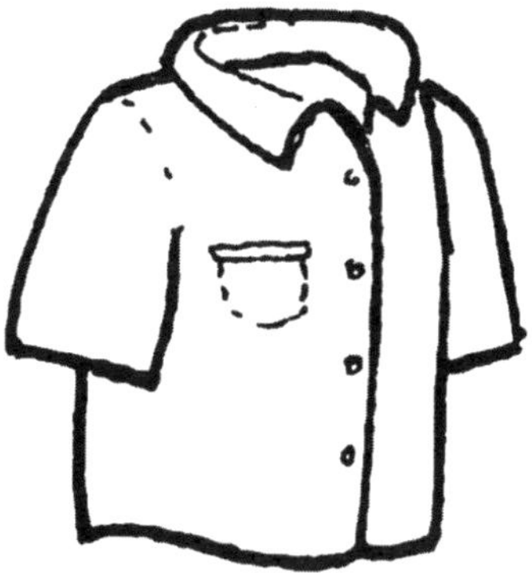

shirt

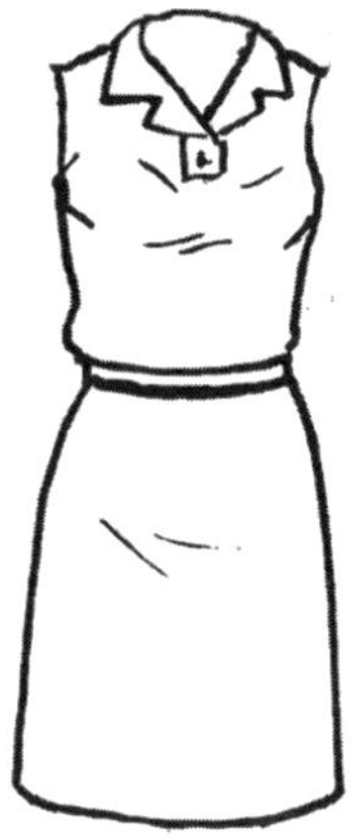

dress

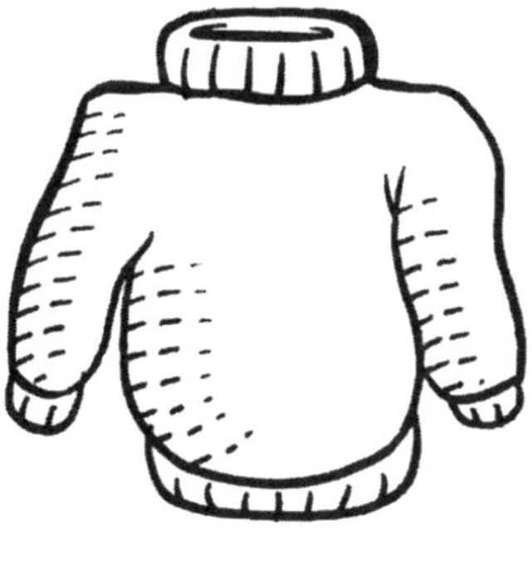

coat

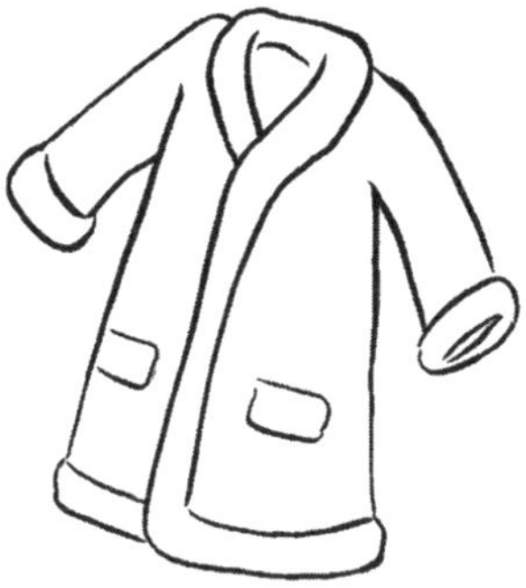

sweater

ELD Standard

Ask and answer simple questions.

ELA Standard

Classify categories of words.

- Ask a partner the questions: *How is he going to school? How are they going to school?*
- Write a sentence to describe how the children are going to school.
- Read the sentences to a partner.

The boy is rideing bike to school.

The school bus is takeing the kids to school.

The boys are walking to school.

ELD Standard
Ask and answer simple questions.
ELA Standard
Write a brief description.

- Circle the picture in each row that shows the person **in front of** an object.
- Write the words "in front of" under the circled picture.
- Ask a partner the question: *Where is the boy? Where is the girl?*
- Answer: *He's in front of the _____ (fence, sofa, bike).*
  She's in front of the _____ (desk).

back

front

front

back

front

back

ELD Standard
Ask and answer simple questions.
ELA Standard
Respond to "*Who, What, When, Where,*" and "*How*" questions.

Identifying Actions

 TO THE TEACHER: Ask students, "**Circle one action in each row.**" Tell them, "**Write a sentence for each action you circled.**"

• Ask a partner the questions: *What is he doing? What is she doing?*

raising his hand

writing

using a computer

She is writing in her notebook.

reading

listening

standing in line

The teacher is reading a story to the kids.

building with blocks

picking flowers

jumping rope

She is jumping rope.

ELD Standard
Produce simple vocabulary to communicate basic needs in social or academic contexts.
ELA Standard
Follow one- and two-step oral directions.

14

Identifying Class Rules

 TO THE TEACHER: Read each rule. Discuss why each rule is important.

• Read the rule to a partner.
• Tell a partner why each rule is important.
• Write your answers on the blank lines.

Raise your hand.

So you can talk.

Don't shout out.

_____

Line up quietly.

_____

Listen to the teacher.

So you know what to do,

ELD Standard
Demonstrate comprehension of simple vocabulary with an appropriate action.
ELA Standard
Ask for clarification and explanation of stories and ideas.

- Ask and answer the question: *Where is the* _____*?*
- Write a sentence to answer each question.
- Read each sentence to a partner.

Where is the computer?

The computer is in the classroom.

Where is the sink?

The sink is in the bathroom.

Where is the chair?

The chair is at my house.

Where is the flag?

The flag is on top of the school.

ELD Standard
Ask and answer simple questions.
ELA Standard
Write a brief description.

- Categorize the objects.
- Write the name of each object in the table.
- Ask a partner the question: **Where's the** _____?

	library	Book
	office	telephone
	bathroom	Sink
	playground	Swing Set

 book √

 telephone √

 sink √

 swing set √

ELD Standard
Ask and answer simple questions.
ELA Standard
Classify categories of words.

TO THE TEACHER: Help students identify the objects on the page. Show them that certain items have more than one form. For example, some pencil sharpeners are attached to a wall; others are small and can fit into a backpack.

- Ask a partner the **"wh"** question: *What's in the backpack?*
- Circle the things that belong in a backpack.
- Discuss why the other objects don't belong in a backpack.
- At the bottom of the page, write a series of words that rhyme with **pack**.
- Read the words to a partner.

- Clap out the syllables of the words.
- Divide the words into syllables.

- Write a sentence for each word.
- Read the sentences to a partner.

cafeteria

_____

ticket

_____

lunch box

_____

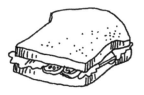

sandwich

_____

ELD Standard
Read simple sentences.
ELA Standard
Use basic syllabication rules.

TO THE TEACHER: Identify the preposition "**in**" and the initial sounds of <u>s</u>andwich, <u>b</u>anana, <u>c</u>ookie, and <u>m</u>ilk.

- Ask a partner the **"wh"** question: *What's in the lunch box?*
- Write the names of the foods in the lunch box.
- Read the words to a partner.

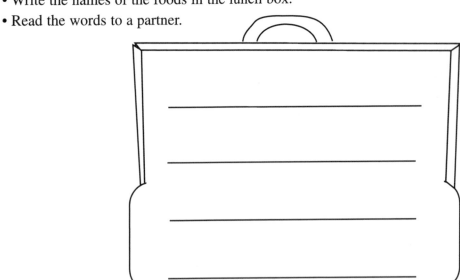

sandwich

banana

cookies

milk

ELD Standard
Answer simple questions using one- or two-word responses.
ELA Standard
Distinguish initial sounds.

- Identify the shapes in each row.
- Identify the circle in row one. Color it blue.
- Find the triangle in row two. Color it yellow.
- Look for the rectangle in row three. Color it orange.
- Color the diamond in row four green.

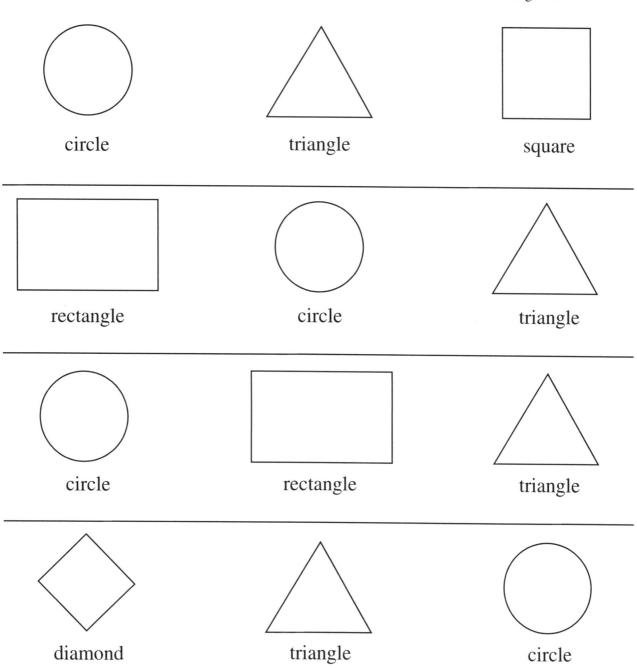

circle   triangle   square

rectangle   circle   triangle

circle   rectangle   triangle

diamond   triangle   circle

ELD Standard
Read simple vocabulary.
ELA Standard
Follow simple two-step directions.

TO THE TEACHER: Teach the **apostrophe** ('s) as a short way of writing **he is - he's, she is - she's.**

- Identify the pronouns in each question.
- Ask a partner the *"wh"* questions: ***Who is he? Who is she?***

Who is she?
She's the mother.

Who is he?
He's the dog.

Who is he?
He's the brother.

Who is he?
He's the father.

Who is she?
She's the mother.

Who is he?
He's the baby.

Who is he?
He's the cat.

Who is she?
She's the sister.

Who is he?
He's the father.

ELD Standard
Demonstrate understanding of simple vocabulary.
ELA Standard
Read compound words and contractions.

22

Identifying Sight Words

Lesson 2.22a

- Identify the sight words ***said, have***, and ***I***.
- Rewrite each sentence and underline the sight words.
- Draw a picture for each sentence.
- Read the sentences to a partner.

The sister said, "I have one cat."

____

The brother said, "I have two dogs."

____

Dad said, "I have three pens."

____

Grandpa said, "I have four books."

____

ELD Standard
Read familiar phrases and simple sentences that follow English syntactical order.
ELA Standard
Read common irregular sight words (e.g., *the, have, said, come, give, of*).

- Tell a partner the names of the pictures that begin with a "g".
- Write the words that begin with a "g" under the correct pictures.

| gate | goat | grapes | girl |

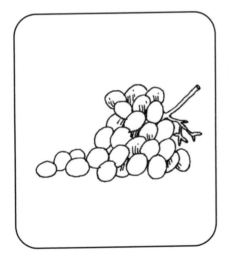  

ELD Standard
Recognize and produce English sounds in contextual vocabulary (pictures).
ELA Standard
Distinguish the initial sounds in single-syllable words.

- Label the families as **large** or **small**. Write the correct underlined word in the first blank.
- In the second blank, write in the total number of members in each family.
- After each picture, ask a partner the question: *Is this family large or small?*
- The partner answers: *This family is _____.*

Is this family large or small?

This family is _____.

There are _____ people in this family.

Is this family large or small?

This family is _____.

There are _____ people in this family.

Is this family large or small?

This family is _____.

There are _____ people in this family.

TO THE TEACHER: Identify the initial consonant sounds **p, m, d, s**. Review the initial consonant sounds **m** through **t**.

- Look at the letters in the box at the right.
- Write the initial consonant sound in each word below.
- Read the words to a partner.

| p | m | d | s |

_____Pot

_____deer

_____Pig

_____Sun

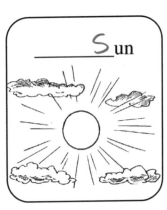

_____Map

_____dog

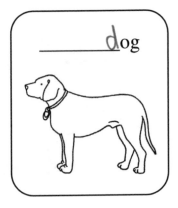

_____mop

_____dish

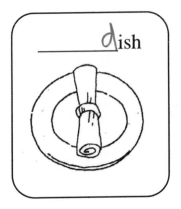

_____Sit

ELD Standard
Demonstrate understanding of sound-symbol relationships.

ELA Standard
Distinguish the initial consonant sounds in single-syllable words.

Identifying *Tall, Taller, Tallest*

Lesson 2.24b

 TO THE TEACHER: Teach **comparatives** and **superlatives**.

- Ask a partner the "**wh**" question: *Who's tall, taller, tallest?*
- Write sentences to describe the pictures. *She is tall. She is taller. She is tallest.*
  He is tall. He is taller. He is tallest.

She is tall.
_____   _____   _____

_____   _____   _____

ELD Standard
Demonstrate understanding of simple vocabulary.
ELA Standard
Respond to "*Who, What, Where, When,*" and "*How*" questions.

- Identify the members of the family.
- Ask a partner the question: *Who is this?*
- Draw a picture of your family tree.

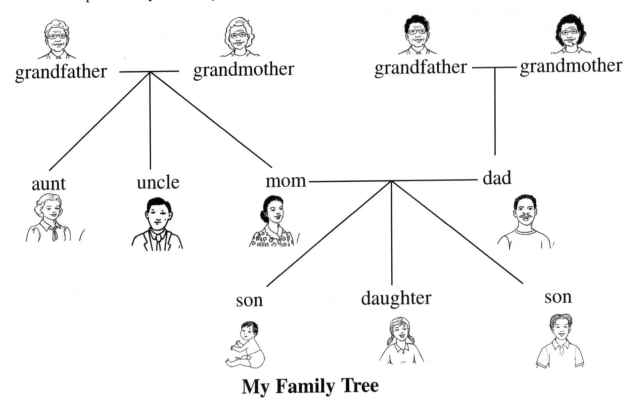

My Family Tree

ELD Standard
Produce simple vocabulary. Read vocabulary aloud.
ELA Standard
Respond to "*Who, What, Where, When,*" and "*How*" questions.

Categorizing

 TO THE TEACHER: Identify and discuss the people and the things they use on their jobs.

- Draw a line from the person to the object that he or she uses on the job.
- Ask a partner the questions: *What's his job? What's her job? What's this?*

carpenter

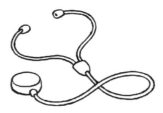

stethoscope

computer programmer

telescope

doctor

hammer

astronomer

keyboard

ELD Standard
Ask and answer questions using simple sentences.
ELA Standard
Respond to "*Who, What, Where, When,*" and "*How*" questions. Identify categories.

Writing Descriptions

 TO THE TEACHER: Teach the **apostrophe** ('s) to indicate possession: *The family belongs to the girl.*

- Ask a partner the questions: *Where does the girl's family live? Where does the boy's family live?*
- Write a sentence to describe where each person lives.
- Read the sentences to a partner.

Where does the girl's family live?

_____

_____

Where does the boy's family live?

_____

_____

Where does the man's family live?

_____

_____

Where does the lady's family live?

_____

_____

ELD Standard
Produce independent writing using correct grammatical forms.
ELA Standard
Group related ideas and maintain a consistent focus.

TO THE TEACHER: Label and discuss the use of the objects on the page.

• Circle the pictures of the things that we mail.
• Ask a partner the question: ***What's this?***
• Write an address on the envelope.
• Ask a partner the question: ***What's your address?***

ELD Standard
Ask and answer simple questions.
ELA Standard
Respond to *"Who, What, Where, When,"* and *"How"* questions.

• Ask a partner the "wh" question: ***Who's talking on the telephone?***

• Write a sentence for each picture.

Who's talking on the telephone?

_____

_____

_____

_____

_____

_____

_____

_____

- Ask a partner the "**wh**" question: *What time is it?*
- Draw a picture and write a phrase to describe what you do in the morning, afternoon and evening.
- Describe the pictures to a partner.

What time is it?	What time is it?	What time is it?

ELD Standard
Respond to simple questions. Identify time on a clock.
ELA Standard
Respond to "*Who, What, Where, When,*" and "*How*" questions. Write brief descriptions.

TO THE TEACHER: Teach the position words **next to, inside, in front of**, and **behind**.

- Draw a picture to illustrate each sentence.
- Rewrite each sentence. Read the sentences to a partner.

The park is <u>next to</u> the library.

_____

_____

Mother is <u>inside</u> the house

_____

_____

The mailbox is <u>in front of</u> the house.

_____

_____

The cow is <u>behind</u> the fence.

_____

_____

ELD Standard Use correct parts of speech, including correct subject/verb agreement. Respond to simple directions using physical actions and other means of non-verbal communication (e.g., matching objects, pointing to an answer, drawing pictures).
ELA Standard Identify and use various parts of speech, including nouns and verbs, in writing and speaking.

Explaining Vocabulary Word Meanings

Lesson 2.31b

 TO THE TEACHER: Teach the parts of speech - nouns and verbs:
> **noun** - the name of a person, place, or thing
> **verb** - action word

- Write **noun** or **verb** for each vocabulary word.
- Draw a picture and write a sentence for each word.
- Describe the pictures and read the sentences to a partner.

Vocabulary Word	Noun or Verb	Picture	Sentence
street			
walk			
school			
neighborhood			
look			

ELD Standard
Use correct parts of speech, including correct subject/verb agreement.
ELA Standard
Identify and use various parts of speech, including nouns and verbs, in writing and speaking.

TO THE TEACHER: Teach **compound words** as two words that are put together. Use knowledge of individual words within each compound word to predict the compound word's meaning.

• Fill in the bubble for each compound word.
• Read the words to a partner.

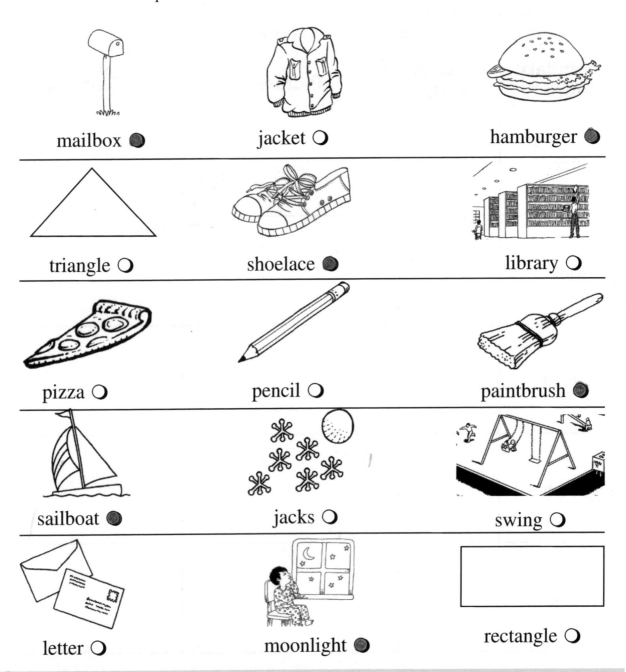

mailbox ●   jacket ○   hamburger ●

triangle ○   shoelace ●   library ○

pizza ○   pencil ○   paintbrush ●

sailboat ●   jacks ○   swing ○

letter ○   moonlight ●   rectangle ○

ELD Standard
Read compound words and contractions.
ELA Standard
Use knowledge of individual words within compound words to predict their meaning.

TO THE TEACHER: Teach punctuation at the end of the sentence.

- Put a question mark, period, or exclamation point at the end of each sentence.
- Read the sentences to a partner.
- Write each sentence with the correct end punctuation.

1. Does Mrs. Brown water the seeds?

   Does Mrs. Brown water the seeds?

2. I plant the seeds.

   I plant the seeds.

3. Wow, that's a big sunflower!

   Wow, that's a big sunflower!

4. I watch the flowers grow.

   I watch the flowers grow.

5. Look at the sunflower.

   Look at the sunflower.

6. Is she watering the seeds?

   Is she watering the seeds?

7. Where is the hose?

   Where is the hose?

ELD Standard
Use a period or question mark at the end of the sentence.
ELA Standard
Distinguish between declarative, exclamatory, and interrogative sentences.

TO THE TEACHER: Read the story to the students. Answer the questions together.

- Listen carefully as your teacher reads you a story.
- Then answer the questions.
- Read the story to a partner. Then ask your partner to retell the story. Switch roles.

The Rock Garden

Mr. Lee has a rock garden.
He has big rocks and little rocks.
The big rocks are boulders.
The little rocks are pebbles.

 1. Mr. Lee has a -
- ○ flower garden.
- ● rock garden.
- ○ big truck.

2. Big rocks are -
- ● boulders.
- ○ pebbles.
- ○ flowers.

 3. This story is about -
- ○ flowers.
- ● rocks.
- ○ people.

 4. The small rocks are -
- ○ apples.
- ● pebbles.
- ○ candles.

ELD Standard Respond orally to stories read to them by answering factual comprehension questions using one- or two-word responses.
ELA Standard
Comprehend informational text.

• Read the story.
• Fill in the bubble for each correct answer.
• Draw a picture for each **underlined** vocabulary word.
• Write the word under the picture.

> Mr. Lee has a rock garden. He has big rocks, or boulders, in his rock garden. He has little rocks, or pebbles, next to his boulders. Some rocks have many colors. They are multicolored. Other rocks are shiny, or polished.

1. A <u>boulder</u> is a kind of -
   - ○ crayon.   ● rock.
   - ○ pencil.   ○ flower.

This is a boulder.

2. <u>Multicolored</u> means -
   - ● many colors.   ○ big.
   - ○ one color.   ○ mean.

These are multicolored rocks.

3. Something that is <u>polished</u> is -
   - ○ old.   ○ rough.
   - ○ yellow.   ● shiny.

This is a polished rock.

4. A <u>pebble</u> is a -
   - ○ large rock.   ○ shoe.
   - ○ pineapple.   ● small rock.

These are pebbles.

ELD Standard
Draw and label pictures related to a story topic or own experience.
ELA Standard
Use knowledge of words to identify meaning.

TO THE TEACHER: Identify living and non-living things.

- Circle all the living things.
- Ask a partner the questions: *Is this a living thing? Does it grow?*
  Does it breathe? Does it drink water?

rock

flower

pail

bird

dustpan

cake

tree

feather

map

ELD Standard
Ask and answer simple questions.
ELA Standard
Categorize groups of words.

Identifying Contractions

 TO THE TEACHER: Teach the **contraction** for **does not - doesn't**.

• Write the correct word in each sentence.
• Read the sentences to a partner.

1. A chair _____ breathe.
   does   doesn't

2. A rock _____ breathe.
   does   doesn't

3. A flower _____ breathe.
   does   doesn't

4. A cat _____ drink milk.
   does   doesn't

5. A mop _____ drink water.
   does   doesn't

6. A tree _____ grow.
   does   doesn't

7. A rock _____ grow.
   does   doesn't

8. A boy _____ grow.
   does   doesn't

9. A gorilla _____ grow.
   does   doesn't

ELD Standard
Read compound words and contractions.
ELA Standard
Identify and correctly use contractions.

TO THE TEACHER: Read the Spelling Friend Card instructions on page 212. Introduce the cards to your students. Teach the long **ā** sound-spelling pattern **_ame** with Spelling Friend Card #1.
Create words by blending the initial consonant sounds to the spelling patterns; for example, /g/ame.
Ask: **What's the word?** Continue with the other words. Discuss the meaning of each word.

• Dictate the words on Spelling Friend Card #1 to a partner. Switch roles.

• Read the words in the box.

• Write the correct word in each sentence. Read the sentences to a partner.

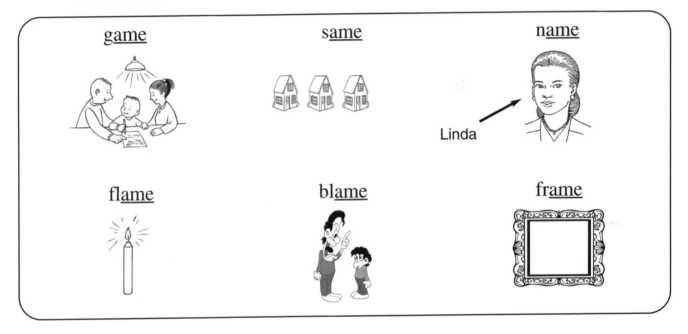

These houses are the _____ .

Linda is her _____ .

The match has a _____ .

The boy is to _____ for starting the fight.

Put the picture in a _____ .

Let's play a card _____ .

TO THE TEACHER: Teach the long ā sound-spelling pattern **_ail** with Spelling Friend Card #2. Create words by blending the initial consonant sounds to the spelling patterns; for example, **/m/ail**. Ask: What's the word? Continue with **/s/ail, /f/ail, /r/ail, /h/ail**. Discuss the meaning of each word.

• Dictate the words on Spelling Friend Card #2 to a partner. Switch roles.
• Read the words in the box.
• Write the correct word in each sentence. Read the sentences to a partner.

1. The train rides on the _____.

2. The postman is going to bring the _____.

3. Can that boat _____?

4. That animal has a long _____.

5. There was a big _____ in the garden.

TO THE TEACHER: Teach the long ā sound-spelling patterns **_ain** and **_ay** with Spelling Friend Cards #3 and #4.

• Dictate the words on Spelling Friend Cards #3 and #4 to a partner. Switch roles.
• Read the words in the box. Discuss the meaning of each word.
• Write the correct word in each sentence. Read the sentences to a partner.

rain   train   chain   Spain

bay   hay   play   clay

1. She is going to open her umbrella when it starts to _____.

2. Can you make a ball out of _____?

3. Do you want to _____ basketball?

4. The man is riding on the passenger _____.

5. That body of water is a _____.

TO THE TEACHER: If necessary, help children identify the vegetables that grow above and below the ground.

- Write the names of the vegetables that grow above the ground and below the ground.
- Ask a partner the questions: *What vegetable is this?*

  Does it grow above or below the ground?

Above Ground	**Below Ground**
* pepper	* potato
* corn	* turnip
* pumpkin	* carrots

potato	pepper	turnip
carrots	corn	pumpkin

ELD Standard
Apply knowledge of content-related vocabulary to discussions.
ELA Standard
Classify categories of words.

TO THE TEACHER: Teach the long ē sound-spelling patterns **_eet** and **_eep** with Spelling Friend Cards #5 and #6. Blend the initial consonant sounds to the spelling patterns **_eet** and **_eep**.

• Dictate the words on Spelling Friend Cards #5 and #6 to a partner. Switch roles.

• Read the words in the box. Discuss the meaning of each word.

• Write the correct word in each sentence. Read the sentences to a partner.

beep   weep   sweep   sheep

feet   beet   greet   sweet

1. Wool comes from _____.

2. The lady is going to _____ her friends.

3. Please _____ the dirt off the stairs.

4. A _____ is a vegetable.

5. She is so unhappy, she is going to _____.

6. The peach tastes _____.

Identifying Comparatives

 TO THE TEACHER: Teach the comparatives **bigger** and **smaller** with concrete objects.

- Fill in the bubble for each correct answer.
- Ask and answer the questions with a partner.

1. Which baseball glove is bigger?

    ○   ○

2. Which boy is smaller?

    ○   ○

3. Which baseball bat is bigger?

    ○   ○

4. Which hat is smaller?

    ○   ○

5. Which tennis shoes are bigger?

    ○   ○

ELD Standard
Ask and answer simple questions.
ELA Standard
Recognize and use comparatives.

TO THE TEACHER: Teach the long ī vowel sound-spelling patterns **_ike** and **_ive** with Spelling Friend Cards #11 and #12. Blend the initial consonant sounds to the spelling patterns **_ike** and **_ive**.

• Dictate the words on Spelling Friend Cards #11 and #12 to a partner.
• Read the words in the box. Discuss the meaning of each word.
• Write the correct word in each sentence. Read the words to a partner.

bike   Mike   hike   like

five   hive   alive   drive

1. Mike is going to ride his ___bike___.

2. The man is going to ___hike___ up the mountain.

3. I have ___five___ fingers on my hand.

4. The bees keep their honey in a ___hive___.

5. Dad is going to ___drive___ the new car.

ELD Standard Generate the sounds from all the letters and letter patterns, including phonograms, and blend these sounds into recognizable words.

ELA Standard Read most common word families. Spell basic short-vowel, long-vowel, r-controlled, and consonant-blend patterns correctly.

Word Families, Spelling Friends _ose, _one Lesson 2.38a

• Dictate the words on Spelling Friend Cards #15 and #16 to a partner. Switch roles. Read the words in the box. Discuss the meaning of each word.

• Write the correct word in each sentence. Read the sentences to a partner.

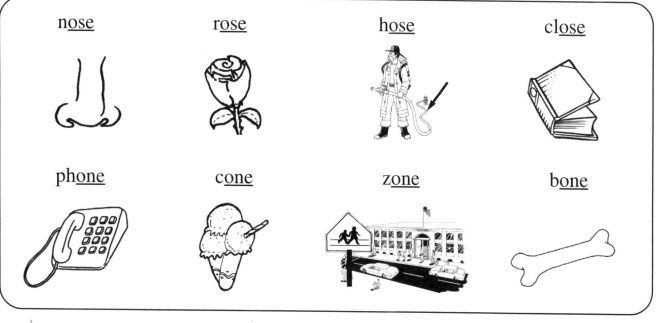

n<u>ose</u>   r<u>ose</u>   h<u>ose</u>   cl<u>ose</u>

ph<u>one</u>   c<u>one</u>   z<u>one</u>   b<u>one</u>

1. You smell with your ___nose___ .

2. Water the plants with the ___hose___ .

3. The little boy is eating an ice cream ___cone___ .

4. Please don't drive fast in the school ___zone___ .

5. The dog is going to eat the ___bone___ .

6. Please ___close___ the door.

Word Families, Spelling Friend Long ō

- Review Spelling Friend Cards #15, #16, #18, and #20.
- Dictate three words from each card to a partner. Switch roles.
- Read the words in the box. Discuss the meaning of each word.
- Write the correct word in each sentence.

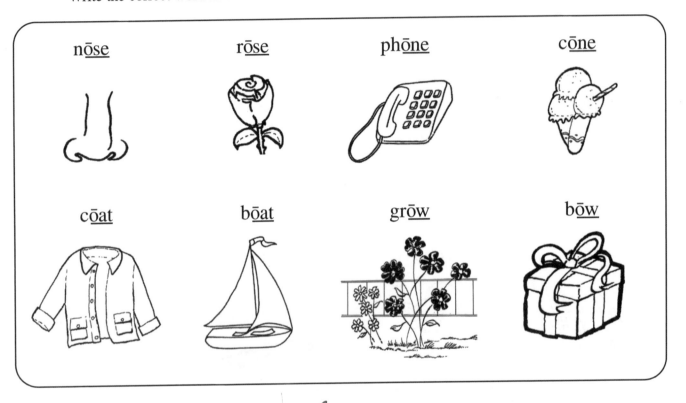

nōse   rōse   phōne   cōne

cōat   bōat   grōw   bōw

1. Maria smells with her _nose_.

2. The red _rose_ smells very nice.

3. I am going to wear my warm _coat_.

4. The people are going down the river in a _boat_.

5. The plant is going to _grow_ taller.

6. Put a _bow_ on the present.

ELD Standard Generate the sounds from all the letters and letter patterns, including phonograms, and blend these sounds into recognizable words.

ELA Standard Read most common word families. Spell basic short-vowel, long-vowel, r-controlled, and consonant-blend patterns correctly.

TO THE TEACHER: Teach the direction words **north, south, east** and **west.**

• Use the compass rose below.
• Ask a partner the question: **What direction is the _____ on the map?**
• Write the correct direction word in each sentence. Read the sentences to a partner.

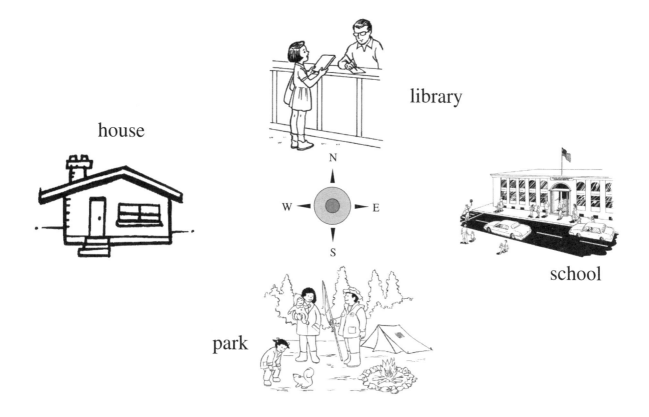

house

library

school

park

1. What direction is the library on the map? The library is _____.

2. What direction is the park on the map? The park is _____.

3. What direction is the school on the map? The school is _____.

4. What direction is the house on the map? The house is _____.

ELD Standard
Ask and answer simple questions.
ELA Standard
Respond to "*Who, What, Where, When,*" and "*How*" questions.

TO THE TEACHER: Teach the long **ū** sound-spelling patterns **_u_e**, **_use** and **_ew** with Spelling Friend Cards #21 and #22. Also, teach the _u_e pattern. Blend the initial consonant sound to the sound-spelling patterns. For example, **/m/ule.**
   Ask: *What's the word?* Continue with **/f/use, /c/ute, /f/ew.**

• Dictate the words on Spelling Friend Cards #21 and #22 to a partner. Switch roles.
• Discuss the meaning of each word in the box below.
• Write the correct word under each picture and in each question.
• Read the words to a partner. Ask and answer the questions with a partner.

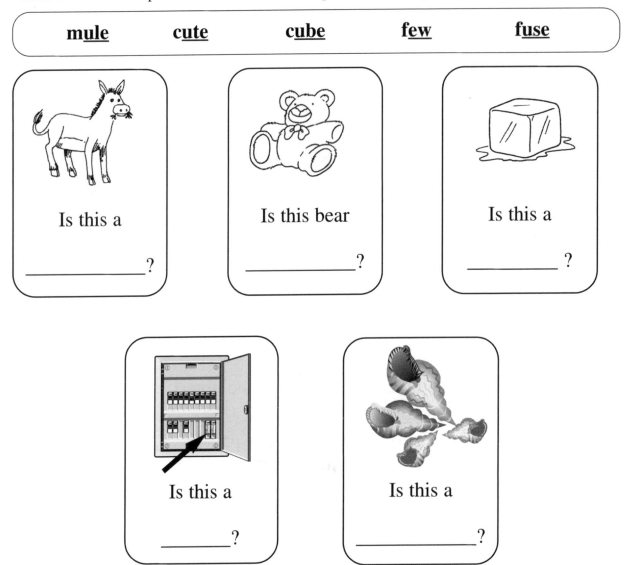

mule	cute	cube	few	fuse

Is this a _____?

Is this bear _____?

Is this a _____?

Is this a _____?

Is this a _____?

Creating Word Maps

 TO THE TEACHER: Before children begin working on this page, discuss what's in a library and in a neighborhood. Show them how to use word maps.

• What can you find in a library and in a neighborhood?
• Write the words on the word maps.
• Then read the words to a partner.

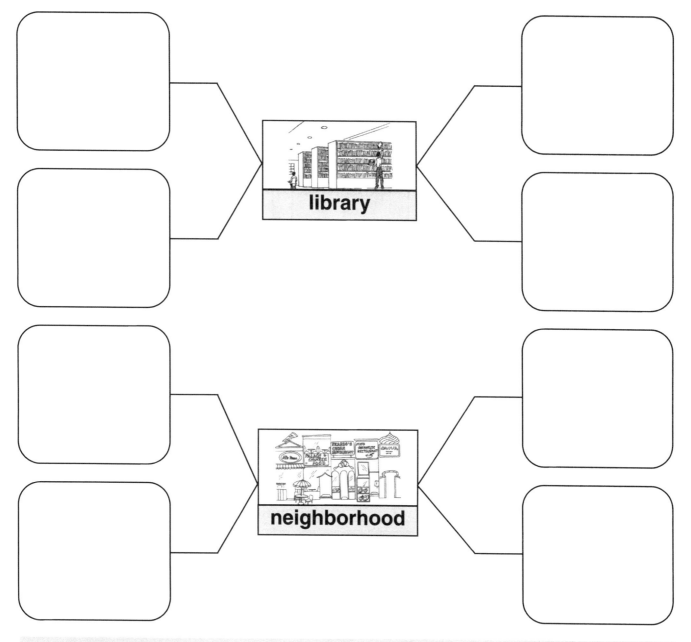

ELD Standard
Read simple vocabulary.
ELA Standard
Group together related ideas, and maintain a consistent focus.

53

TO THE TEACHER: Teach the short ă sound-spelling pattern _at with Spelling Friend Card #23. Blend the initial consonant sounds to the sound-spelling pattern.

• Dictate the words in the box below to a partner. Switch roles.
• Then draw a picture for each circled word.
• Write the correct short ă sound word in each sentence.
• When you are finished, read the sentences to a partner.

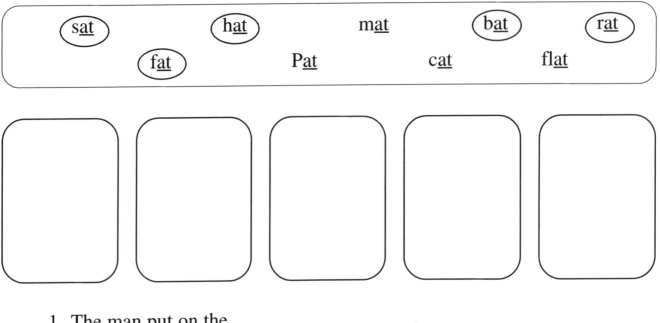

1. The man put on the _____.

2. The cat is _____.

3. He hit the ball with a _____.

4. She _____ in the chair.

5. The dog is chasing the _____.

ELD Standard Recognize English sounds presented in contextual vocabulary.
ELA Standard Distinguish short vowel sounds in single-syllable words. Spell basic short-vowel, long-vowel, r-controlled, and consonant-blend patterns correctly.

54

TO THE TEACHER: Teach the short **ă** sound-spelling pattern **_an** with Spelling Friend Card #24. Blend the initial consonant sound to the spelling pattern: **/m/an, /c/an, /p/an, /v/an, /r/an, /f/an**. Discuss the meaning of the words in the box.

- Dictate the words on Spelling Friend Card #24 to a partner. Switch roles.
- Write the correct short **ă** sound word under each picture.
- Read the words to a partner.

man   **can**   **pan**   **van**   **ran**   **fan**

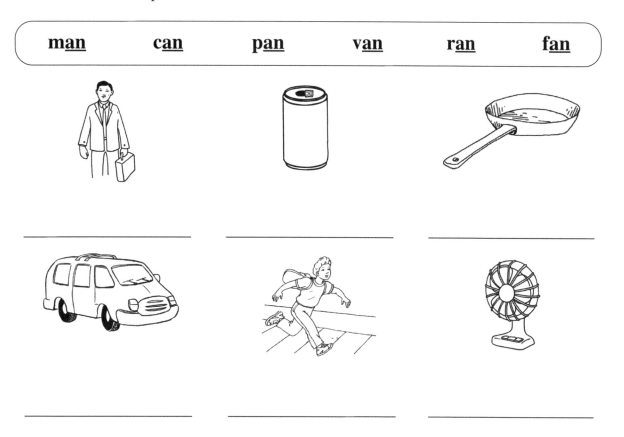

Draw a picture for this sentence:

The man has a trash can in his van.

- Read the questions first. Then read the passage together.
- Fill in the bubble for each correct answer.
- Read the passage to a partner.
- Ask your partner to retell the story.
- Switch roles.

Margarita's City Neighborhood

Margarita lives in a city neighborhood. She lives in an apartment building with ten floors. Margarita works in a factory. The factory is across the river from the city. She crosses the bridge every day to get to work.

1. Margarita's apartment has -
   - ○ two floors.
   - ○ five floors.
   - ● ten floors.
   - ○ twenty floors.

2. Why does Margarita cross the bridge every day?
   - ○ to go shopping
   - ○ to visit a friend
   - ○ to go to the zoo
   - ● to get to work

3. The writer wrote this story to tell about -
   - ● where Margarita lives and works.
   - ○ where factories are in the city.
   - ○ where apartments can be found.
   - ○ how to cross a bridge.

4. Margarita lives in the -
   - ● city.
   - ○ country.
   - ○ factory.
   - ○ houseboat.

ELD Standard Respond orally to simple stories by answering factual comprehension questions using phrases or simple sentences.
ELA Standard
Use knowledge of the author's purpose to comprehend information in the text.

Identifying Multiple Word Meanings

Lesson 2.41b

• Fill in the bubble for the sentence where the word has the same meaning.
• Read the sentences to a partner.
• Discuss the different meanings of the words.

1. Margarita can <u>cross</u> the river.

   In which sentence does the word <u>cross</u> mean the same as in the sentence above?
   - ○ Cross out the wrong answer.
   - ● He can't cross the street.
   - ○ Cross the "t".
   - ○ Mother was cross when we were late.

2. How many <u>steps</u> must Margarita climb to get to the tenth floor?

   In which sentence does the word <u>steps</u> mean the same thing as in the sentence above?
   - ○ He took five steps in the mud.
   - ○ Run up the steps.
   - ○ There are four steps to making cookies.
   - ● She steps lightly on the new grass.

3. The baseball <u>batter</u> hit a home run.

   In which sentence does the word <u>batter</u> mean the same thing as in the sentence above?
   - ○ A bumpy road can batter you up.
   - ○ She is mixing the cake batter.
   - ○ The puppies love to batter each other around.
   - ● He is the next batter coming up to bat.

ELD Standard
Recognize words with multiple meanings in text.
ELA Standard
Identify simple multiple-meaning words.

TO THE TEACHER: Teach the short ă sound-spelling patterns **_ask** and **_and** with Spelling Friend Cards #26 and #27. Blend the initial consonant sound to the spelling patterns.

• Dictate the words from Spelling Friends Cards #26 and #27 to a partner. Switch roles.
• Read the words in the box. Discuss the meaning of each word.
• Write the correct word in each sentence. Read the sentences to a partner.

mask   ask   task   flask

hand   band   stand   sand

1. The man is wearing a ___mask___ over his eyes.

2. She is going to ___ask___ the teacher a question.

3. Taking out the trash is his ___hand___.

4. I am going to put the water in a ___flask___.

5. The ___band___ is going to play music.

6. I have five fingers on my ___hand___.

7. Carlos is going to the beach to play in the ___sand___.

8. Please ___stand___ up.

ELD Standard Generate the sounds from all the letters and letter patterns, including phonograms, and blend these sounds into recognizable words.

ELA Standard Read most common word families. Spell basic short-vowel, long-vowel, r-controlled, and consonant blend patterns correctly.

Word Families, Spelling Friends _ox and _op   Lesson 2.42a

• Dictate the words from Spelling Friend Cards #28 and #29 to a partner.
• Switch roles.
• Write the correct word in each sentence. Read the sentences to a partner.

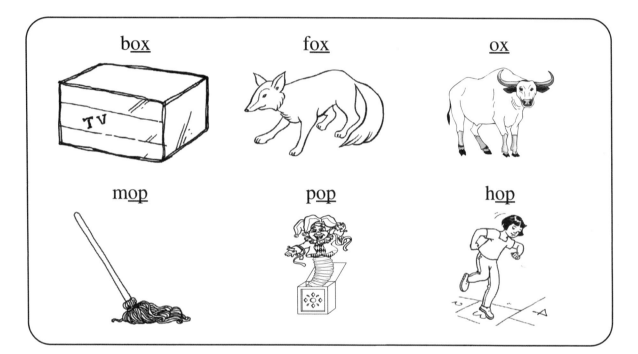

box   fox   ox

mop   pop   hop

1. The birthday present is in a _____.

2. The _____ can run very fast.

3. The _____ can pull a cart.

4. Dad cleans the floor with a _____.

5. I can _____ on one foot.

6. Jack is going to _____ out of the box.

• Read the questions first, and then read the passage together.

• Fill in the bubble for each correct answer.

• Read the passage to a partner. Then ask your partner to retell the story. Switch roles.

City Rules

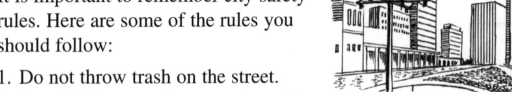

It is important to remember city safety rules. Here are some of the rules you should follow:

1. Do not throw trash on the street.
2. Cross the street only at a crosswalk.
3. Look both ways for cars before you cross the street.
4. Obey all traffic signs.
5. Ride your bike only in the bike lanes.

1. These rules tell how to -
   - ○ play a game.
   - ○ ride a bike.
   - ○ bake a cake.
   - ○ be safe.

2. You will need rule 5 only if you -
   - ○ cross the street.
   - ○ drive a car.
   - ○ ride a bike.
   - ○ walk to school.

3. What should you do before you cross the street?
   - ○ put on your helmet.
   - ○ listen for a siren.
   - ○ start running.
   - ○ look both ways for cars.

4. Which of these is one way to follow rule #1?
   - ○ look both ways before crossing the street.
   - ○ stop at the corner.
   - ○ use a trashcan.
   - ○ cross at a crosswalk.

5. You do not need some of these rules if you -
   - ○ ride a bike.
   - ○ never go to the city.
   - ○ drive a car.
   - ○ ride a motorcycle.

ELD Standard Respond orally to simple stories by answering factual comprehension questions using phrases or simple sentences.

ELA Standard
Use knowledge of the author's purpose to comprehend information in the text.

TO THE TEACHER: Discuss the places in Margarita's neighborhood. Review the position words **next to**.

• Ask and answer the questions with a partner.

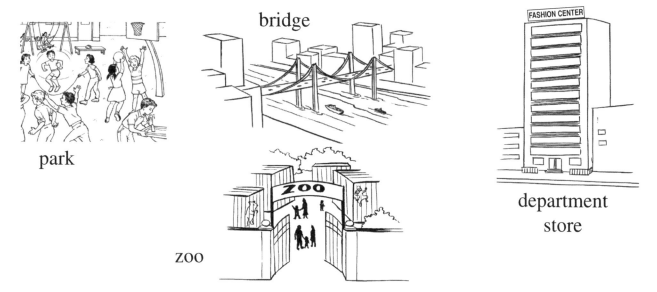

park

bridge

zoo

department store

1. Where is the zoo? The zoo is next to the _____.

2. Where is the department store?

   The department store is next to the _____.

3. Where is the park? The park is next to the _____.

4. Where is the bridge? The bridge is next to the _____.

ELD Standard
Ask and answer questions.
ELA Standard
Ask "*Who, What, Where, When*" and "*How*" questions.

Identifying Short ă and Long ā Vowel Sounds Lesson 2.43b

• Listen as the teacher says the words in the box.

• Write the correct word in each box. On the lines, write a sentence for each word.

• Read the sentences to a partner.

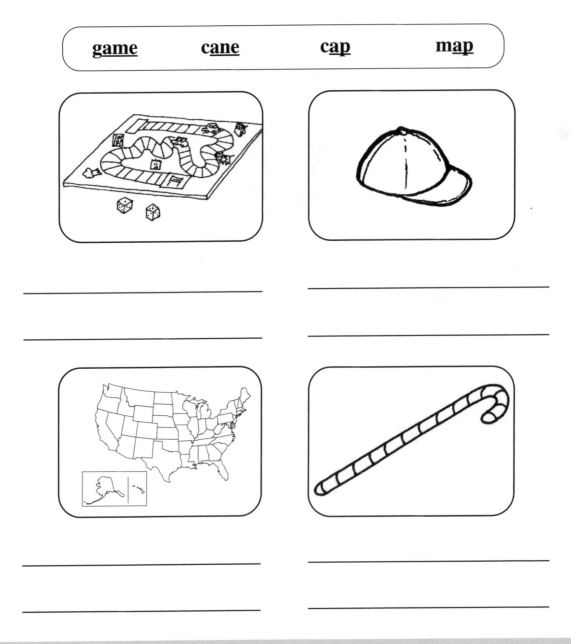

| game | cane | cap | map |

TO THE TEACHER: Teach the short ŏ sound-spelling pattern _ot with Spelling Friend Card #30. Blend the initial consonant sounds.

• Dictate the words on Spelling Friend Card #30 to a partner. Switch roles.
• Then list words that rhyme with each underlined letter pattern below.
• Underline the short ŏ or long ō sound-spelling pattern in each word.
• Read the words to a partner.

gŏt

lŏt

pŏt

dŏt

hŏt

bŏx

fŏx

tŏp

nōse

pōke

hōle

ELD Standard
Distinguish long- and short-vowel sounds in orally stated single-syllable words.
ELA Standard
Identify short- and long-vowel sounds.

• Read the story.
• Identify the characters, setting, problem, and solution.
• Answer the questions on the next page.
• Then make a story map with pictures.
• Retell the story to a partner.

Juan's Paints

High in the mountains of Peru lies the village of Arbol Grande. It is a small village of clay adobe houses alongside a river in a grassy field. Juan Esparto lives in an adobe house. Each day, he walks to an adobe one-room school. Today, everyone in the one-room school is going to learn how to paint a picture.

Juan is very sad. He will not be able to paint a picture because he doesn't have any paints. His family does not have the money to buy paints. Juan doesn't want to go to school without paints.

Juan's mother comforts Juan. She tells him that the country people of Peru often make their own paints. She tells Juan, "You can get black from the charcoal of a burned tree. You can get blue from the blueberries that grow by the river. You can get yellow from the dried sunflowers in the meadow. You can get red from the clay on the ground."

Juan thanks his mother. Juan goes outside. He finds a burned tree. He takes some of the charcoal to make black paint. He finds the blueberries to make blue paint. He finds sunflowers to make yellow paint. He finds red clay on the ground to make red paint.

He takes the things home and creates the paint colors in four bowls. Juan happily takes the four bowls to school. Now, he too can paint a picture with his class.

Creating a Story Map

Lesson 2.44c

Who is the main character?

___

What is the setting of the story?

___

What was the problem?

___

What was the solution?

___

Story Map (draw and label the pictures)

Main Character

Problem

Setting

Solution

ELD Standard
Retell simple stories using drawings, words, or phrases.
ELA Standard
Identify character, setting, problem, and solution.

• Read the questions first, and then read the passage together.

• Fill in the bubble for each correct answer.

• Read the story to a partner. Ask your partner to retell the story. Switch roles.

Skyscrapers

There are many skyscrapers in big cities. A skyscraper is a very tall building. Some skyscrapers have twenty floors. You need to go up in an elevator to get to the top floor. The top floor of a skyscraper usually has an observation deck. You can look down from the observation deck of a skyscraper onto all the smaller buildings in the city.

1. This story was written to -
   ○ tell what an elevator is used for.
   ○ get you to buy something.
   ○ tell about tall buildings in the city.
   ○ show how to do something.

2. Another good name for this story is -
   ○ A Walk in the Park.
   ○ An Elevator Ride.
   ○ A City Tour.
   ○ Tall Buildings in the City.

3. What is the best way to find out more about skyscrapers?
   ○ build a tall building out of blocks
   ○ read a book about skyscrapers
   ○ take an elevator in a store
   ○ take a bus ride

4. In this story, an observation deck is a place where -
   ○ you can take a plane.
   ○ you can look down on the city.
   ○ cars can drive.
   ○ people can learn to drive.

ELD Standard Read and use detailed sentences to orally identify the main idea and use the idea to draw inferences about text.

ELA Standard
Use knowledge of the author's purpose to comprehend information in the text.

TO THE TEACHER: Teach the sight word <u>where</u> and high frequency words <u>on</u> and <u>the</u>.

• Write the questions on the lines below.
• In each question, underline the word <u>where</u>.
• Ask and answer the questions with a partner.
• Draw a picture to illustrate each answer.

1. Where is the train?

_____

The train is <u>on the</u> track.

2. Where is the car?

_____

The car is <u>on the</u> road.

3. Where is the roof?

_____

The roof is <u>on the</u> house.

4. Where is the book?

_____

The book is <u>on the</u> table.

5. Where is the cat?

_____

The cat is <u>on the</u> hat.

ELD Standard
Read simple one-syllable and high-frequency words.
ELA Standard
Identify irregular sight words and high frequency words.

• Read the questions first, and then read the passage together.
• Fill in the bubble for each correct answer.
• Read the story to a partner. Then ask your partner to retell the story. Switch roles.

Bus Rules

It is important to remember safety rules when you ride the city bus. Here are the rules you should follow:

1. Do not stick your arms out the window.
2. Sit down in a seat.
3. Wait on the sidewalk for the bus.
4. Do not push people when you get off the bus.
5. Do not disturb the bus driver.

1. The rules tell you how to -
   ○ play a game.
   ○ ride a bike.
   ○ play baseball.
   ○ be safe.

2. Which of these is one way to follow rule 1?
   ○ watch for cars
   ○ put your bags under the seat
   ○ keep your hands in your lap
   ○ stand up

3. What should you <u>not</u> do when you get off the bus?
   ○ push
   ○ walk
   ○ stand still
   ○ cross the street at a green light

4. In this story, the word <u>disturb</u> means -
   ○ walk.
   ○ bother.
   ○ distance.
   ○ safe.

ELD Standard
Use the content of a story to draw logical inferences.
ELA Standard
Distinguish main ideas and supporting details in expository text.

Word Families, Spelling Friends _ed and _en   Lesson 2.46b

• Dictate the words on Spelling Friend Cards #31 and #32 to a partner. Switch roles.
• Write the correct word in each sentence. Read the sentences to a partner.

bed   Ned   sled   shed

hen   pen   ten   men

1. I sleep in a _____.

2. That boy's name is _____.

3. Put the rake in the _____.

4. Ned and Fred slide down the hill on a _____.

5. Fred is going to write with a _____.

6. I have _____ fingers.

7. The eggs are from the _____.

8. Dad and Mike are _____.

- Read the questions first, and then read the passage together.
- Fill in the bubble for each correct answer.
- Read the story to a partner. Then ask your partner to retell the story. Switch roles.

Zoo Animals

Juan and his brother, Roberto, went to the city zoo. They first went to see the gorillas. The gorillas were eating bananas. Next, they went to see the tigers. The tigers were walking around their cages. Finally, they went to see the alligators. The alligators were floating in the water. After seeing all the animals, Juan and his brother went home.

1. Where does this story take place?
   - ○ at the park
   - ○ at the zoo
   - ○ at school
   - ○ in the market

2. The boxes show some things that happened in the story.

They went to see the gorillas.		They went to see the alligators.
1	2	3

Which of these belongs in box 2?
   - ○ They took the bus home.
   - ○ They went to see the tigers.
   - ○ They walked home.
   - ○ They went to see the monkeys.

3. This story was written to -
   - ○ show how alligators swim.
   - ○ tell what gorillas eat.
   - ○ tell about a day at the zoo.
   - ○ tell about a bus ride.

4. Which of these animals did Juan and Roberto not see at the zoo?
   - ○ gorilla
   - ○ alligator
   - ○ giraffe
   - ○ tiger

ELD Standard
Use the content of a story to draw logical inferences.
ELA Standard
Recall major points in text, and make and modify predictions about forthcoming information.

Word Families, Spelling Friends _et and _ent Lesson 2.47b

- Dictate the words from Spelling Friend Cards #33 and #34 to a partner. Switch roles.
- Write the correct word under each picture and in each sentence.
- Read the words and sentences to a partner.

> p<u>et</u>   n<u>et</u>   m<u>et</u>   w<u>et</u>
> <u>cent</u>   <u>tent</u>   <u>dent</u>   <u>rent</u>

_____

Catch the fish in the _____.

_____

The rain made the street _____.

_____

A penny is one _____.

_____

The camp has a _____.

TO THE TEACHER: Show visuals and discuss different types of city transportation.

• Make a mind map of city transportation.
• Write a sentence about each type of transportation.
• Read the sentences to a partner.

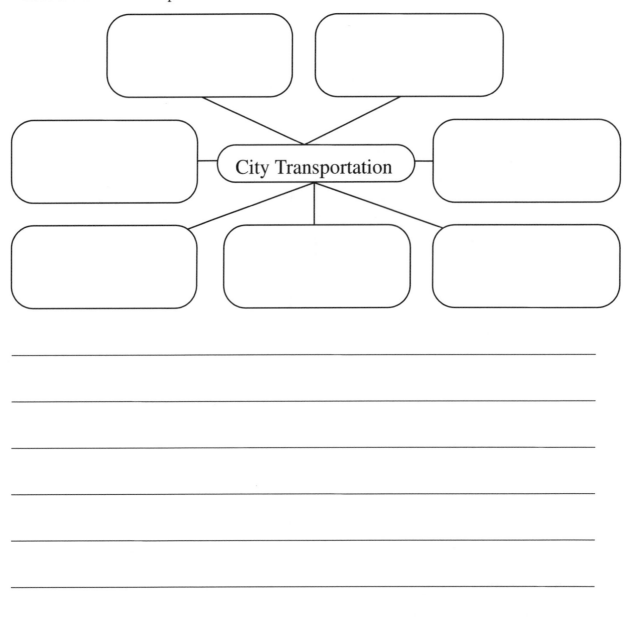

City Transportation

_____

_____

_____

_____

_____

_____

ELD Standard
Apply knowledge of content-related vocabulary to discussions and reading.
ELA Standard
Categorize groups of words.

TO THE TEACHER: Teach the short **ŭ** sound-spelling pattern **_ug** and **_un** with Spelling Friend Cards #35 and #36. Blend the initial consonant sounds to the spelling pattern. Discuss the meaning of each word.

- Dictate the words from Spelling Friend Cards #35 and #36 to a partner.
- Read the words in the box.
- Write the correct word in each sentence.
- Read the sentences to a partner.

1. Put the water in a _____.

2. A beetle is a _____.

3. That is the hole he _____.

4. Yellow is the color of the _____.

5. We are going to have _____ at the party.

6. She is going to _____ home.

7. Put the hamburger in the _____.

• Read the questions first, and then read the passage together.
• Fill in the bubble for each correct answer.
• Read the recipe to a partner. Then ask a partner to describe how to make peanut butter.

Peanut Butter

Time needed: 20 minutes
You will need:

     2 cups of peanuts
     1 tablespoon sugar
     1 teaspoon salt

1. Grind the peanuts.
2. Put in the salt and sugar.
3. Blend on high speed in the blender.
4. Put the mixture in a jar.
5. Eat the peanut butter with jam on toast. You can also put the peanut butter in chocolate chip cookie mix, and make peanut butter chocolate chip cookies.

1. People eat peanut butter on toast with -
   - ○ candy.
   - ○ jam.
   - ○ ice.
   - ○ steak.

2. When you make peanut butter, the spoons are used to -
   - ○ measure.
   - ○ hold the peanut butter.
   - ○ blend the ingredients.
   - ○ shell the peanuts.

3. After you grind the peanuts and put in the salt and sugar, you should -
   - ○ put the peanuts in a bag.
   - ○ eat the bread.
   - ○ put everything in the blender.
   - ○ stir the salt.

ELD Standard
Use the content of a story to draw logical inferences.
ELA Standard
Distinguish main ideas and supporting details in expository text.

- Discuss what is happening in each picture.
- Finish the story.
- Use the writing checklist on page 253 to edit your work.
- Read the story to a partner.

1

2

3

The girl is going to make a sandwich. _____

_____

_____

_____

_____

_____

_____

ELD Standard
Edit writing for basic conventions and make some corrections.
ELA Standard
Move through a logical sequence of events.

Word Families, Spelling Friends _it and _ish Lesson 2.49c

 TO THE TEACHER: Teach the short ĭ sound-spelling patterns **_it** and **_ish** with Spelling Friend Cards #39 and #40. Blend the initial consonant sounds to the spelling patterns.

• Dictate the words from Spelling Friend Cards #39 and #40 to a partner.

• Read the words below. Discuss the meaning of each word.

• Draw a picture for each word. Read the words to a partner.

| sit | bit | hit | fish | wish | dish |

sit	bit
hit	fish
wish	dish

TO THE TEACHER: Teach the sound-spelling pattern **_ig** and **_ive** with Spelling Friend Cards #41 and #44.

- Discuss the meaning of each word below. Read the words to a partner.
- Write the correct word in each riddle.
- Read the riddles to a partner.

---

twig   fig   pig   wig   liver   give   river   sliver

---

1. It is a fruit. It is a _____.

2. It is on the branch of a tree. It is a _____.

3. You see this animal on a farm. It is a _____.

4. You put it on your head. It is a _____.

5. A motorboat travels on this. It is a _____.

6. It is a small piece of something. It is a _____.

7. You can eat this for dinner. It is _____.

8. This is a verb that means "to transfer something to someone."

   It is to _____.

• Read the questions first, and then read the passage together.
• Fill in the bubble for each correct answer.
• Read the story to a partner. Then ask your partner to retell the story. Switch roles.

Jam Factory

Grape jam was made at the jam factory today. First, the seeds were taken out of the grapes. Next, the grapes were cooked in large pots with sugar. The grape liquid was cooled and poured into jars. Labels were put on the jars. The jars of grape jam were packed into boxes. The jars of grape jam were taken by truck to the market.

1. This story was written to -
   ○ tell how jam is made.
   ○ show how to attach labels.
   ○ get you to buy something.
   ○ tell you how to play a game.

2. What is the best way to find out more about how to make jam?
   ○ read a book about factories
   ○ read a science book
   ○ have a party
   ○ read a cookbook

3. What will the jam factory probably make tomorrow?
   ○ peanut butter
   ○ jam
   ○ cookies
   ○ ice cream

4. What is the first step in making jam?
   ○ grind the cherries
   ○ put in sugar
   ○ put the jam in jars
   ○ take out the seeds

ELD Standard
Use a variety of comprehension strategies.
ELA Standard
Use knowledge of the author's purpose to comprehend information in the text.

TO THE TEACHER: Discuss types of transportation.

• Categorize the types of transportation as flying in the air, driving on the road, or running on a track.
• Write each word under the correct category.

Air	Road	Track
_____	_____	_____
_____	_____	_____
_____	_____	_____
_____	_____	_____

train	limousine	car
light rail	plane	bus
helicopter	jet	subway train
rocket	bicycle	elevated train

- Read the questions first, and then read the passage together.
- Fill in the bubble for each correct answer.
- Read the story to a partner. Then ask your partner to retell the story. Switch roles.

The Lost Suitcase

"Dad, I can't find my suitcase!" Maria called from the bedroom.

"Look in the hall closet," said Dad.

Maria looked in the hall closet. She found coats, umbrellas, shoes and her stuffed rabbit, Fluffy, but she didn't find her suitcase.

"Look in the garage," said Dad.

Maria looked in the garage. She found bicycles, toys and tools. She didn't find her suitcase.

"Where did you put your suitcase?" asked Dad.

Maria thought and thought. Then, finally, she remembered. She had put it under her bed. She looked under her bed. There it was. Maria found her suitcase.

1. Where did Maria look for her suitcase first?

   ○ at the park   ○ at school
   ○ in the garage   ○ in the hall closet

2. The boxes show some things that happened in the story:

Maria looked in the hall closet.		Maria looked under her bed.
1	2	3

   Which of these belongs in box 2?

   ○ Maria found her stuffed bear.
   ○ Maria looked in the garage.
   ○ Maria looked in the kitchen.
   ○ Maria looked in the living room.

3. What lesson does Maria need to learn?

   ○ Clean the garage.
   ○ Always go to bed early.
   ○ Do your homework.
   ○ Put things in the right place.

4. In this story, Fluffy is the name of Maria's -

   ○ stuffed bear.   ○ stuffed rabbit.
   ○ cat.   ○ friend.

5. What is this story about?

   ○ a trip
   ○ a garage sale
   ○ a stuffed rabbit
   ○ Maria's lost suitcase

ELD Standard
Use the content of the story to draw logical inferences.
ELA Standard Restate facts and details in text to clarify and organize ideas.
Recognize cause-and-effect relationships in a text.

• Read the questions first, and then read the passage together.
• Fill in the bubble for each correct answer.
• Read the story to a partner. Then ask your partner to retell the story. Switch roles.

The Light Rail

Mr. Ramirez rides the light rail from the Main Street Station to work everyday. Mr. Ramirez works at City Hall on 17th Street. He gets on the light rail every morning at 8:00 AM.

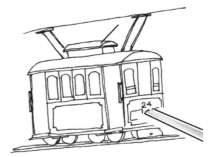

The light rail is a small train that runs on electricity. The following is the light rail time schedule of arrivals at different stations in the neighborhood.

Light Rail Schedule

Departures			Arrivals	
Main Street	8:00 AM		Chestnut Street	8:10 AM
			2nd Street	8:20 AM
			5th Street	8:30 AM
			17th Street	8:45 AM
			22nd Street	8:50 AM

1. What is another good name for this story?
   ○ The Main Street Station
   ○ The Electric Train
   ○ City Hall
   ○ The Airline Schedule

2. Where does the light rail stop first?
   ○ Chestnut Street
   ○ 5th Street
   ○ 2nd Street
   ○ 22nd Street

3. The boxes show some things that happened in the story.

The light rail stops at 2nd Street.		Mr. Ramirez arrives at 17th Street at 8:45.
1	2	3

4. Which of these belongs in Box 2?
   ○ The light rail leaves Main Street.
   ○ The light rail stops at 5th Street.
   ○ The light rail stops at Chestnut Street.
   ○ The light rail stops at 22nd Street.

ELD Standard
Use the content of the story to draw logical inferences.
ELA Standard
Interpret information from diagrams, charts, and graphs.

TO THE TEACHER: Teach the short ŭ spelling pattern _umb with Spelling Friend Card #38. Review the long ū and the short ŭ sounds with Spelling Friend Cards #21, 36, and 37. Identify the short and long sound-spelling patterns for each word in the box. Blend each initial consonant sound to the spelling patterns.

- Dictate the words in the box to a partner.
- Draw a picture for each sentence.
- Write the correct word in each riddle.
- Read the riddles to a partner.

| m<u>u</u>le | f<u>u</u>se | s<u>u</u>n | n<u>umb</u> | cr<u>umb</u> | t<u>u</u>b | l<u>u</u>nch | th<u>umb</u> |

1. It is in the sky.

It is the _____.

3. You take a bath in it.

It is a _____.

2. It is an animal.

It is a _____.

4. It is on your hand.

It is a _____.

ELD Standard
Distinguish long- and short-vowel sounds in orally stated single-syllable words.
ELA Standard Read most common word families. Spell basic short-vowel, long-vowel, r-controlled, and consonant blend patterns correctly.

TO THE TEACHER: Discuss how a ferryboat takes people and cars across water. Teach the meaning of departures, arrivals, AM and PM. Show pictures of ferries and maps showing ferryboat routes.

• Read the chart. Discuss what time the first and last ferryboats leave.
• Ask and answer the questions together.

Pier 4 Ferryboat	Departures-Vallejo	Arrivals-San Francisco
Ferryboat 1	8:30 AM	10:30 AM
Ferryboat 2	11:00 AM	2:00 PM
Ferryboat 3	3:00 PM	5:00 PM
Ferryboat 4	6:00 PM	8:00 PM

1. What time does the first ferryboat leave? It leaves at _____.

2. How many hours does it take Ferryboat 1 to get to San Francisco? _____

3. How many hours does it take Ferryboat 2 to get to San Francisco? _____

4. What time does the last ferryboat leave? _____

5. What time does Ferryboat 3 arrive in San Francisco? _____

6. What time does Ferryboat 4 leave? _____

7. What ferryboat takes the longest time to get to San Francisco? _____

8. What time does Ferryboat 2 arrive in San Francisco? _____

ELD Standard Read and identify text features such as title, table of contents, chapter headings, diagrams, charts, glossaries, and indexes in written texts.
ELA Standard
Interpret information from diagrams, charts, and graphs.

Asking and Answering *How* Questions

Lesson 2.53b

 TO THE TEACHER: Discuss the feelings of each person and the words in the box.

- Point to each picture. Ask a partner: ***How is he feeling? How is she feeling?***
- Write the word to describe how each person is feeling.

angry	happy	dizzy	scared	tired	sad

_____

_____

_____

_____

_____

_____

ELD Standard
Ask and answer simple questions with one- or two-word responses.
ELA Standard
Respond to "*Who, What, Where, When,*" and "*How*" questions.

84

Spelling Friend Digraph sh_

 TO THE TEACHER: Teach the digraph **sh_** with Spelling Friend Card #45. Blend the digraph **sh_** to the sound spelling pattern to create words. Read the words in the box below to the children. Discuss the meaning of each word.

- Dictate the words on Spelling Friend Card #45 to a partner. Switch roles.
- Write the correct word in each sentence. Then read the sentences to a partner.
- Draw a picture for each sentence.

~~ship~~   ~~sheet~~   ~~shine~~   ~~shell~~   ~~show~~   ~~shut~~

The ___Ship___ is going to sail.

The sun is going to ___Shine___.

I am going to the ___Show___.

Put the ___Sheet___ on the bed.

Please ___Shut___ the door.

The ___Shell___ is on the beach.

ELD Standard
Recognize sound-symbol relationships and basic word formation rules.
ELA Standard
Distinguish the consonant digraph **sh_**.

TO THE TEACHER: Read the poem together.

- Read the poem to a partner.
- Underline the rhyming words.
- Ask and answer the questions with a partner.

The City Port

There are ships and boats that come into the city port everyday.
Do you know how many ships and boats are coming into the city port today?
There is a freighter that is blue.
It is bringing cars and bicycles, too.
There is a fishing boat that is red.
It is bringing home my dad, Fred.
There is a silver sightseeing boat with the number ten.
It is coming into the city port with women and men.

1. There are ships and boats that come into the -
   ○ city shopping mall.
   ○ city street.
   ● city port.
   ○ city park.

2. Which of these pairs of words from the poem rhyme?
   ○ blue, ten
   ○ dad, men
   ● red, Fred
   ○ too, today

3. Which of these lines from the poem have words that begin with the same letter and sound?
   ○ There is a silver sightseeing boat number ten.
   ○ It is bringing cars and bicycles, too.
   ● It is bringing home my dad, Fred.
   ○ There is a freighter that is blue.

4. What is the poem about?
   ○ a fishing boat
   ○ a freighter coming into the city port
   ◉ a sightseeing boat
   ● ships and boats that come into the city port

ELD Standard
Identify rhyming words.
ELA Standard
Identify rhyme, rhythm, and alliteration in poetry.

TO THE TEACHER: Discuss the meaning of the underlined words in context.

• Fill in the bubble for the correct meaning of each word.
• Read the sentences to a partner.

1. The ferryboat came into the port. <u>Port</u> means -
   ○ ship.
   ○ plum.
   ● harbor.
   ○ boat.

2. The big ship was carrying freight to the port. <u>Freight</u> means -
   ● cargo.
   ○ fixed.
   ○ funny.
   ○ railroad.

3. The ship was carrying only one car, but it was carrying numerous bikes. <u>Numerous</u> means -
   ○ funny.
   ○ two.
   ● many.
   ○ noisy.

4. The new regulations state that the ship can stay in the port for only one day. <u>Regulations</u> means -
   ○ price.
   ● rules.
   ○ boats.
   ○ signal.

5. Since the ship hadn't used the crane before, the man had to demonstrate how to use the crane to pick up the boxes. <u>Demonstrate</u> means -
   ○ carry.
   ● show.
   ○ buy.
   ○ sell.

6. The captain of the ship stayed on the ship and wouldn't emerge until the ship was docked. <u>Emerge</u> means -
   ● come out.
   ○ sleep.
   ○ eat.
   ○ run.

ELD Standard
Recognize words with multiple meaning in text.
ELA Standard
Identify the meaning of words in context.

87

• Read the questions first, and then read the passage together.
• Fill in the bubble for each correct answer.
• Read the story to a partner. Then ask your partner to retell the story. Switch roles.

Railroad Day

My name is Maylee. Today is a special day in our small village in China. It is Railroad Day. It is to celebrate the day the first railroad came to our village. All the people in the village go down to the railroad station to wait for the train. Everyone brings a flag made of colored cloth. The villagers give the flags to the passengers on the train.

I made a purple flag with a picture of a train on it. I gave my flag to a lady on the train. The lady gave me a piece of candy wrapped in red paper. This afternoon, I will go to the village park with my family for a picnic. Later, we will see the Railroad Day fireworks celebration.

1. This story was written to -
   ○ tell what China looks like.
   ● tell how to make flags.
   ○ tell what people do on one day.
   ○ get you to buy something.

2. What will Maylee do later?
   ○ read a book
   ● watch fireworks
   ○ play baseball
   ○ go to the zoo

3. What is the best way to find out more about China?
   ○ Make a flag for Railroad Day.
   ○ Talk to someone from Japan.
   ○ Buy some fireworks from China.
   ● Read a book about countries.

4. In this story, passenger means a -
   ● someone riding on a train.
   ○ a porter.
   ○ a person riding a bike.
   ◐ a driver.

5. Maylee's flag was -
   ○ big.
   ● purple.
   ○ blue.
   ○ wrinkled.

ELD Standard
Use the content of the story to draw logical inferences.
ELA Standard
Use knowledge of the author's purpose to comprehend information in the text.

Identifying Consonant Blends

 TO THE TEACHER: Teach the consonant blend **tr_**. Blend the **tr_** sound to make words. Discuss the meaning of each word in the box.

- Say: *train, truck, track, trip, tree, trick, and trout.*
- Write the correct word under each picture. Read each word to a partner.

> ~~train~~   ~~truck~~   ~~track~~   ~~trip~~
> ~~tree~~   trick   ~~trout~~

trian

truck

track

tree

trip

trout

ELD Standard
Produce English sounds that correspond to sounds students already hear and produce.
ELA Standard Generate the sounds from all the letters and letter patterns, including consonant blends and long- and short-vowel patterns, and blend these sounds into recognizable words.

Adding a Suffix

 TO THE TEACHER: Discuss the meaning of the words <u>slide</u>, <u>glide</u>, <u>smile</u>, <u>bike</u>, and <u>wipe</u>. Review the rule for adding suffixes: *If a word ends in –e, drop the –e before adding –ing.*

• Add the **_ing** suffix to each word.
• Use each word in a sentence.
• Read the sentences to a partner.

ride

riding

I am riding the bus to school.

slide

I went down the slide.

glide

An airplane is glideing in.

smile

I see Carlose smileing.

bike

I am going bikeing.

- Read the questions first, and then read the passage together.
- Fill in the bubble for each correct answer. Read the passage to a partner.

Frequent Flyer Club

Who Can Join:
Anyone who takes trips on an airplane.

What To Do:

1. Fill out a frequent flyer application.
2. Go on airplane trips.
3. Fill out a coupon for each trip you take.

Coupon
Name:_____
Address:_____
Flight to:_____ From:_____ Date:_____

4. Mail the coupon to the Frequent Flyer Club, Baltimore, Maryland.
5. Club members who send in eight coupons get a free trip anywhere in the United States.

1. To join the club, you should first –
   - ○ take an airplane trip.
   - ○ mail in the coupon.
   - ○ fill out an application.
   - ○ fill out the coupon.

2. To get a free trip, you must mail in –
   - ○ one coupon.
   - ○ eight coupons.
   - ○ ten coupons.
   - ○ an application.

3. Who can join the club?
   - ○ anyone who travels by train only
   - ○ anyone who travels by car only
   - ○ children only
   - ○ anyone who travels by airplane

4. Each coupon asks for –
   - ○ your address.
   - ○ your age.
   - ○ your school.
   - ○ your phone number.

ELD Standard
Use the content of the story to draw logical inferences.
ELA Standard
Distinguish the main idea and supporting details in expository text.

TO THE TEACHER: Teach the consonant blend **pl_**. Blend the **pl** sound to make the following words: **plane, play, plus, plate, please, plant, plaid, plow, plank**. Discuss the meaning of each word.

- Write the correct word under each picture.
- Read the words to a partner.

> **plane**   **play**   **plus**   **plate**   **please**   **plant**   **plow**

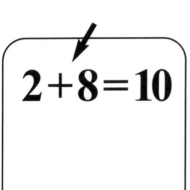

_____

_____

_____

_____

_____

ELD Standard
Recognize and use knowledge of spelling patterns.
ELA Standard Generate the sounds from all the letters and letter patterns, including consonant blends and long- and short-vowel patterns, and blend these sounds into recognizable words.

TO THE TEACHER: Teach the words <u>arrival</u> and <u>departure</u>.

• Use the airplane arrival and departure chart to answer the questions.
• Ask and answer the questions with a partner.
• Write the answers in complete sentences.

ARRIVALS		DEPARTURES	
From:	Time	To:	Time
New York City, New York	9:30 AM	Miami, Florida	10:00 AM
Chicago, Illinois	11:00 AM	Salt Lake City, Utah	11:30 AM
Las Vegas, Nevada	3:00 PM	Tucson, Arizona	2:00 PM
San Antonio, Texas	4:30 PM	Boston, Massachusetts	6:00 PM
Los Angeles, California	7:00 PM	Detroit, Michigan	8:00 PM

1. What time will Grandpa's plane arrive from New York City?

   It will arrive at _____.

2. What time will Aunt Maria leave for Tucson, Arizona?

   _____.

3. What time will the singer arrive from Las Vegas, Nevada?

   _____.

4. What time will the skiers leave for Salt Lake City, Utah?

   _____.

5. What time will the pilot leave for Miami, Florida?

   _____.

ELD Standard Read and identify text features such as title, table of contents, chapter headings, diagrams, charts, glossaries, and indexes in written texts.
ELA Standard
Interpret information from diagrams, charts, and graphs.

Identifying Consonant Blends

 TO THE TEACHER: Teach the consonant blends **tr_** and **pl_**. Blend the **tr_** and **pl_** sounds into words: **tr**ain, **tr**uck, **tr**ash, **tr**iangle, **tr**ip, **pl**ane, **pl**ay, **pl**ate, **pl**ant.

- Write the correct word under each picture.
- Read the words to a partner.

train	truck	trash	triangle	trip

plane   play   plate   plant

 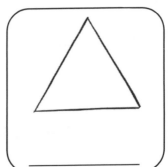 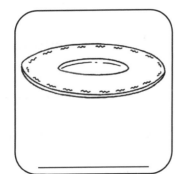

ELD Standard
Recognize and use knowledge of spelling patterns.
ELA Standard Generate the sounds from all the letters and letter patterns, including consonant blends and long- and short-vowel patterns, and blend these sounds into recognizable words.

- Read the questions first, and then read the passage together.
- Fill in the bubble for each correct answer.
- Read the passage to a partner.

Planes

Ever since planes were made, people have been trying to get planes to fly faster.

At first, planes could only fly short distances at a slow speed. The first planes were flown in open fields. They took off from dirt runways. The pilots wore special eyeglasses called "goggles" to protect their eyes. The cockpit, in the front of the plane, was open. There were no windows to keep out the dust. The pilot had to crank the plane's engine to get it started.

Today, planes fly very fast. Jets travel at 500 miles per hour. Pilots use computers to help them fly the plane. Control towers help guide the plane as it takes off.

1. Another good name for this story is –
   - ○ A Fast Race.
   - ○ Flying High in the Sky.
   - ○ Planes Long Ago.
   - ○ Planes Then and Now.

2. The writer wrote this story to tell –
   - ○ how planes have changed.
   - ○ how dirt got in the pilot's eyes.
   - ○ how fast planes fly.
   - ○ how computers fly planes.

3. Special eyeglasses that protect the pilot's eyes are –
   - ○ muffs.
   - ○ sunglasses.
   - ○ goggles.
   - ○ lenses.

4. In this story, a <u>cockpit</u> is a place where –
   - ○ planes are parked.
   - ○ pilots sit to fly the plane.
   - ○ planes are sent to be repaired.
   - ○ planes are painted.

ELD Standard
Use the context of the story to draw logical inferences.
ELA Standard
Use knowledge of the author's purpose to comprehend information in a text.

TO THE TEACHER: Teach the digraphs **th_**, **ch_**, and **wh_** with Spelling Friend Cards #46, #47 and #48. Blend the digraphs to create words. For example, **/th/ird**. Read the words in the box. Discuss the meaning of each word.

- Dictate the words on the Spelling Friend Cards #46, #47 and #48 to a partner. Switch roles.
- Write the correct word in each sentence.
- Read the sentences to a partner.

<u>third</u>	<u>th</u>in	<u>th</u>ong	<u>ch</u>ief	<u>ch</u>ip	<u>wh</u>ale

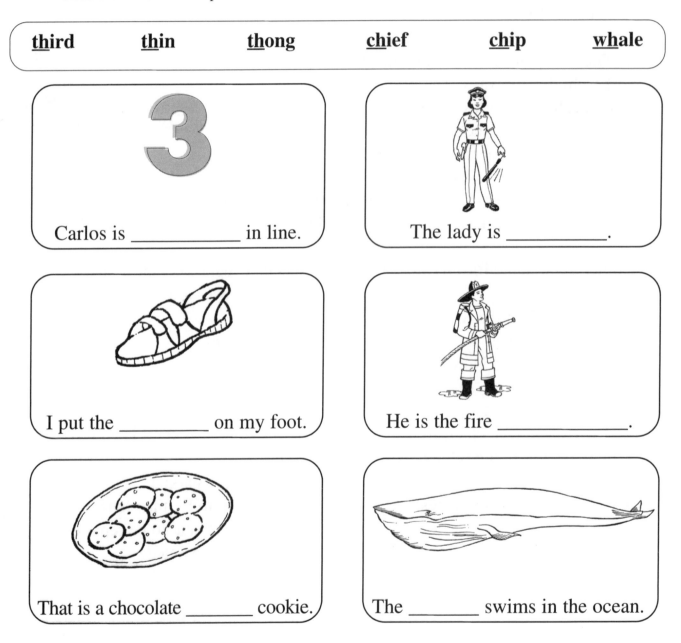

Carlos is _____ in line.

The lady is _____.

I put the _____ on my foot.

He is the fire _____.

That is a chocolate _____ cookie.

The _____ swims in the ocean.

ELD Standard
Blend two or more phonemes into recognizable words.
ELA Standard Distinguish consonant digraphs **th_**, **ch_**, **wh_**. Spell basic short-vowel, long-vowel, r-controlled, and consonant-blend patterns correctly.

Categorizing

 TO THE TEACHER: Compare and contrast travel today with travel long ago.

- Write the words for the transportation that was used long ago and today.
- Ask the questions: *What transportation was used long ago?*
                     What transportation is used today?

Transportation Long Ago

_____

_____

_____

Transportation Today

_____

_____

_____

Space Shuttle

Horse and Buggy

Model T Ford

Bi-Plane

Bullet Train

Jet

ELD Standard
Ask and answer instructional questions with more extensive supporting details.
ELA Standard
Categorize groups of words.

- Describe what is happening in each picture.
- Finish the story.
- Use the writing checklist on page 253 to edit your work.
- Read the story to a partner.

1

2

3

A Visit to Grandma's

The family is getting into the car. They are going to visit Grandma.

_____

_____

_____

_____

_____

_____

TO THE TEACHER: Teach the _ar spelling pattern with Spelling Friend Card #49. Blend the initial consonant sounds to the spelling pattern _ar to create words; for example, **/j/ar**. Read the words in the boxes. Discuss the meaning of each word.

• Dictate the words on Spelling Friend Card #49 to a partner. Switch roles.
• Read the words in the boxes below. Discuss the meaning of each word.
• For numbers 1-5 below, write the **ar** in each word. Then write a sentence for each word.

star
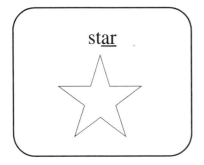

jar

far

car
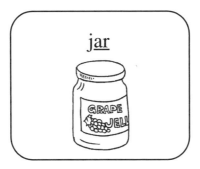

bar
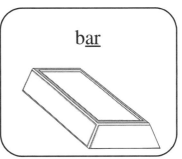

1. st___   _____

2. c___   _____

3. j___   _____

4. b__   _____

5. f___   _____

ELD Standard
Use knowledge of vowel digraphs r-controlled, letter-sound associations to read words.
ELA Standard Spell basic short vowel, long vowel, r-controlled, and consonant blend patterns correctly. Spell basic short-vowel, long-vowel, r-controlled, and consonant-blend patterns correctly.

• Read the questions first, and then read the passage.
• Fill in the bubble for each correct answer.
• Read the passage to a partner. Then ask your partner to retell the story. Switch roles.

Travel In The Future

How will people travel in the future? They will travel on the freeway in spacemobiles. They will travel in spacemobiles above the ground so they can look around. They will travel in their spacemobiles to the spaceport. They will take a spaceship from the spaceport to the moon. Do you think that spaceships will be ready to leave from the spaceport in your city soon?

1. Another good title for this story is –
   ○ Planes and Trains.
   ○ Spaceships and Space People.
   ○ Future Clothes.
   ○ Future Transportation.

2. The writer wrote this story to tell –
   ○ how rockets will take off.
   ○ how people will travel in the future.
   ○ how people will dress in the future.
   ○ how fast planes will fly in the future.

3. Spacemobiles are future –
   ○ bikes.
   ○ homes.
   ○ cars.
   ○ trains.

4. In this story, a spaceport is a place where –
   ○ cars get repaired.
   ○ homes are made for the future.
   ○ rockets take off for the moon.
   ○ trains come into the station.

5. In the future, people will travel in –
   ○ tubes.
   ○ cars.
   ○ space helmets.
   ○ spacemobiles.

ELD Standard
Use the content of the story to draw logical inferences.
ELA Standard
Use knowledge of the author's purpose to comprehend information in a text.

TO THE TEACHER: Teach the **_arm** sound-spelling pattern with Spelling Friend Card #50. Blend the sounds into recognizable words. Read the words in the box. Discuss the meaning of each word.

• Dictate the words on Spelling Friends Card #50 to a partner. Switch roles.
• Write the correct word in each riddle. Read the riddles to a partner.

arm
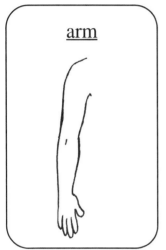

farm

alarm

charm

1. Your hand is at the end of it. It is an _____.

2. This is on a bracelet. It is a _____.

3. A rooster lives on it. It is a _____.

4. It wakes you up in the morning. It is an _____.

ELD Standard
Blend two or more phonemes into recognizable words.
ELA Standard
Spell basic short-vowel, long-vowel, r-controlled, and consonant blend patterns correctly.

Explaining Word Meaning

 TO THE TEACHER: Discuss recycling and its role in creating a clean and safe neighborhood. Review nouns and verbs.

- Label each word as a **noun** or a **verb**. Draw a picture and write a sentence for each word.
- Describe the picture, and read the sentences to a partner.

Vocabulary Word	Noun or Verb	Picture	Sentence
neighborhood			
mow			
recycle			
bottles			
cans			

ELD Standard
Apply knowledge of content-related vocabulary.
ELA Standard
Identify and correctly use various parts of speech, including nouns and verbs, in writing and speaking.

Word Families, Spelling Friends _an and _ask Lesson 2.61b

• Dictate the words on Spelling Friend Cards #24 and #27 to a partner.
• Write the correct word in each sentence. Read the sentences to a partner.

ran	Dan	tan	pan
ask	task	mask	flask

1. His name is _____.

2. The color of his shirt is _____.

3. Carlos _____ in the race.

4. Maylee cooks the fish in a frying _____.

5. The boy's _____ is to mow the lawn.

6. Will you _____ her to your birthday party?

7. Put the _____ over your eyes.

8. A little bottle is a _____.

ELD Standard
Blend two or more phonemes to create words. Read common word families.
ELA Standard
Spell basic short vowel, long vowel, r-controlled, and consonant blend patterns correctly.

• Read the questions first, and then read the passage together.
• Fill in the bubble for each correct answer.
• Read the passage to a partner.
• Then ask your partner to retell the story. Switch roles.

Recycling Day

Do you know what recycling means? It means to use again. It is important to recycle bottles and cans so they can be used again.

Every week, on Wednesday, all the families on our street put out our plastic bottles and cans in separate recycling containers. A big red truck picks up the plastic bottles. A big green truck picks up the cans.

The big red truck takes the plastic bottles to a recycling factory. The factory has lots of big machines. The first machine washes the bottles. The second machine cuts the bottles into tiny pieces. The third machine cooks the plastic pieces in hot water. The last machine makes the plastic pieces into pellets. Finally, these plastic pellets are sent to other factories to make new plastic bottles.

1. What happens first to the plastic bottles?
   ○ They are filled with milk.
   ○ They are heated.
   ○ They are washed.
   ○ They are cut up.

2. This story was written to tell you -
   ○ why people should run.
   ○ what happens to recycled bottles.
   ○ how machines work.
   ○ where trucks take the cans.

3. In this story, the word <u>recycle</u> means -
   ○ give bottles a new name.
   ○ put bottles in containers.
   ○ use something again.
   ○ make something out of paper.

4. What happens to plastic bottles picked up by the red truck?
   ○ They are taken to families.
   ○ They are taken to a recycling factory.
   ○ They are taken to the dump.
   ○ They are taken to the store.

5. Recycling containers are picked up -
   ○ on Sunday.
   ○ in the middle of the week.
   ○ at the end of the week.
   ○ every other week.

6. Plastic pellets are used to make -
   ○ cans.
   ○ plastic bottles.
   ○ glass jars.
   ○ paper cups.

ELD Standard
Retell simple stories.
ELA Standard
Use knowledge of the author's purpose to comprehend information in a text.

TO THE TEACHER: Discuss the recycling process as seen in the pictures.

- Describe what is happening in each picture.
- Finish the story.
- Use the writing checklist on page 253 to edit your work.
- Read the story to a partner.

1   2   3

The Recycling Process

This is recycling day on our street.

_____

_____

_____

_____

_____

ELD Standard
Edit writing for basic conventions and make some corrections.
ELA Standard
Move through a logical sequence of events.

• Read the questions first, and then read the passage together.
• Fill in the bubble for each correct answer.
• Read the passage to a partner. Then ask your partner to retell how to join the Recycling Club. Switch roles.

Sierra Neighborhood Recycling Club

<u>Who Can Join:</u>
Anyone who lives in the Sierra neighborhood and wants to collect bottles and cans.

<u>What To Do:</u>
1. Fill out an application.
2. Take the application to Mr. Gomez at the Sierra Community Center.
3. Fill in a coupon for every 20 bottles or cans you collect.

Coupon
Name:_____
Address:_____

4. Put the coupons in the Recycling Club box at the Sierra Community Center.
5. Club members who fill out eight coupons get a free trip to the zoo.

---

1. To join the club, you should first -
   ○ go to the zoo.
   ○ fill out an application.
   ○ see Mr. Gomez.
   ○ fill out the coupon.

2. To get a free trip to the zoo, you must fill out -
   ○ one coupon.   ○ four coupons.
   ○ two coupons. ○ eight coupons.

3. Who can join the club?
   ○ only boys
   ○ only girls
   ○ anyone who lives in the Sierra neighborhood
   ○ anyone who goes to school

4. Each coupon shows -
   ○ your address. ○ your school.
   ○ your age.   ○ your picture.

ELD Standard
Retell simple stories.
ELA Standard
Determine the main idea and supporting details in expository text.

Abbreviations for the Days of the Week

Lesson 2.63b

Lesson 2.63b

 TO THE TEACHER: Teach the abbreviations for the days of the week. Then teach abbreviations as a short way of writing the word.

- Write the "short way" or abbreviation for each day of the week.
- Write a sentence about something you do on each day.

Day	Abbreviation
Sunday	Sun.
Monday	Mon.
Tuesday	Tues.
Wednesday	Wed.
Thursday	Thurs.
Friday	Fri.
Saturday	Sat.

1. Sunday   Sun.   I walk the dog on Sunday. _____

2. Monday _____ _____

3. Tuesday _____ _____

4. Wednesday _____ _____

5. Thursday _____ _____

6. Friday _____ _____

7. Saturday _____ _____

ELD Standard
Recognize common abbreviations.
ELA Standard
Identify abbreviations for days of the week and months of the year.

• The graph shows how many cans each family recycled last week.
• Answer each question in a complete sentence.
• Read and discuss your answers with a partner.

Recycled Cans

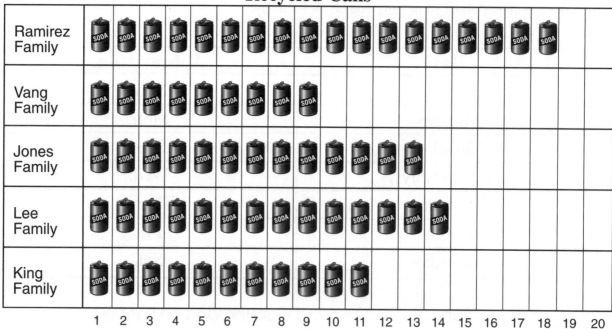

1. How many cans did the Lee family recycle?_____

2. How many cans did the Vang family recycle?_____

3. Which family recycled the fewest cans?_____

4. Which family recycled the most cans?_____

5. Why do you think the Ramirez family recycled the most cans?

_____

_____

Capitals and End Punctuation

> **TO THE TEACHER:** Review the use of capitals for **words at the beginning of a sentence**, **days of the week** and **a person's name**. Review the use of end punctuation: A **period** goes after a statement. A **question mark** goes after a question. An **exclamation mark** goes after a sentence expressing emotion.

- Rewrite the sentences.
- Put in capitals and ending punctuation.

1. antonio rides his bike to school on monday

   _____

2. samantha eats lunch with mary on tuesday

   _____

3. where do you go to eat on wednesday

   _____

4. is today thursday or friday

   _____

5. grandpa goes fishing on friday

   _____

6. wow, what a great day I had saturday

   _____

7. grandma is coming to visit on sunday

   _____

ELD Standard Use capital letters to begin sentences and proper nouns. Use a period or question mark at the end of a sentence.
ELA Standard
Capitalize words at the beginning of a sentence. Use end punctuation.

> **TO THE TEACHER:** Review the meaning of **recycling** - to use again. Discuss why bottles and cans are recycled. Read the poem and questions together.

- Fill in the bubble for each correct answer.
- Read the poem to a partner. Underline the rhyming words.
- Ask your partner to retell the main idea of the poem. Switch roles.

Recycling Bottles and Cans

Let's collect bottles and cans -
red, yellow and blue.
We can clean up the park and
make money, too.
We can sell the cans for three cents each.
We can sell the big bottles for two cents more.
We can get our money at
the recycling center in our neighborhood store.

1. <u>Recycling</u> means -
   - ○ to use again.
   - ○ to run around.
   - ○ to buy a dress.
   - ○ to find a dog.

2. Which of these pairs of words from the poem rhyme?
   - ○ too, each
   - ○ more, store
   - ○ each, more
   - ○ blue, store

3. What is the poem about?
   - ○ cans
   - ○ money
   - ○ recycling
   - ○ a store

4. Which of these lines from the poem have words that begin with the same letter?
   - ○ We can clean up the park and make money, too.
   - ○ Let's collect bottles and cans.
   - ○ We can sell the cans for three cents each.
   - ○ We can sell the big bottles for two cents more.

ELD Standard
Identify and produce rhyming words.
ELA Standard
Identify rhythm, rhyme, and alliteration in poetry.

TO THE TEACHER: Teach the sight words <u>water</u>, <u>would</u>, <u>were</u>, <u>pull</u>. Then teach the words <u>neighborhood</u> and <u>beautification</u>. Clap out the syllables with students. Discuss how flower gardens make a neighborhood beautiful.

• Read the question first. Then read the passage. Fill in the bubble for each correct answer.
• Read the passage to a partner. Then ask your partner to retell the story. Switch roles.

Making the Neighborhood Beautiful

Today is Neighborhood Beautification Day. All the people in our neighborhood are working in their gardens. They are working to make our neighborhood beautiful.

Mrs. Jones is planting flowers and vegetables in her garden. She is using a small shovel called a trowel to dig a hole. Mr. Lee is trimming the bushes. He is using big clippers. Mrs. Garcia is digging a hole for a peach tree with a shovel. Mr. Jackson is using a hose to water the grass. Mrs. Jackson is pulling the weeds around the roses. Ms. Fox is trimming bushes and raking leaves. Mrs. Carlo is using a watering can to water the flower pots. All the neighborhood gardens are looking beautiful. Does your family have a garden? What would you do to make your family's garden beautiful?

1. What day is it?
   ○ Neighborhood Beautification Day
   ○ Mother's Day
   ○ Neighborhood Recycling Day
   ○ Columbus Day

2. What does Mrs. Jones do to make her garden beautiful?
   ○ trim bushes
   ○ water the trees
   ○ plant flowers and vegetables
   ○ pull weeds

3. What would be another good title for this story?
   ○ How to Plant Trees
   ○ Using Garden Tools
   ○ Making the Roses Grow
   ○ Neighborhood Beautification Day

4. What is the story about?
   ○ a beautiful rose garden
   ○ neighbors working to recycle cans
   ○ neighbors working to make the neighborhood beautiful
   ○ pulling weeds

ELD Standard
Retell simple stories.
ELA Standard
Use knowledge of the author's purpose to comprehend information in text.

- Discuss what is happening in each picture.
- Finish the story.
- Use the writing checklist on page 253 to edit your work.
- Read the story to a partner.

1

2

3

The girl plants the seeds. _____

_____

_____

_____

_____

_____

Adding a Suffix

 TO THE TEACHER: Teach the meaning of a **suffix**. Discuss how suffixes change word meaning.
Review the rule: **If a word ends in _e, drop the _e before adding _ed or_ing.**

- Fill in the chart.
- Choose a word from the chart to fill in the missing word in each sentence.
- Read the sentences to a partner.

Root Word	Add suffix _ed	Add suffix _ing
play		
use		
name		
bake		
learn		
arrange		
work		
describe		

1. He _____ baseball yesterday.

2. She _____ the scissors yesterday.

3. Miguel is _____ how the new house looks.

4. Pao _____ his puppy Spot.

5. She is _____ how to cook.

6. Is Mom _____ the flowers in a vase?

7. Linda _____ the cake this morning.

8. Tom _____ at the factory yesterday.

ELD Standard
Use simple suffixes attached to known vocabulary.
ELA Standard
Know the meaning of simple suffixes.

TO THE TEACHER: Review Spelling Friend Card #4. Blend the initial consonant sounds to the sound-spelling patterns. Discuss the meaning of the words in the box.

- Dictate the words on Spelling Friend Card #4 to a partner. Switch roles.
- Write the missing **_ay** spelling pattern in each word. Write the words in the sentences.
- Then read the sentences to a partner.

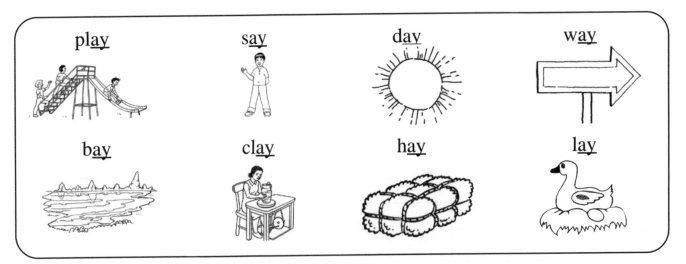

play   say   day   way

bay   clay   hay   lay

pl___   1. What game did you _____ today?

h___   2. The horse is eating _____.

cl___   3. The flower pot is made of _____.

l___   4. The hen will _____ an egg.

d___   5. How was your _____?

b___   6. A _____ is a body of water.

s___   7. What did the boy _____?

w___   8. Which _____ is north?

TO THE TEACHER: Teach the spelling pattern **_eigh** and **_eight** with Spelling Friend Cards #51 and #52. Blend the initial consonant sounds to the sound-spelling patterns. Discuss the meaning of each word in the box.

- Dictate the words on Spelling Friend Cards #51 and #52 to a partner.
- Write the missing **_eigh** or **_eight** spelling pattern in each word.
- Write the word in the sentence.
- Then read the sentences to a partner.

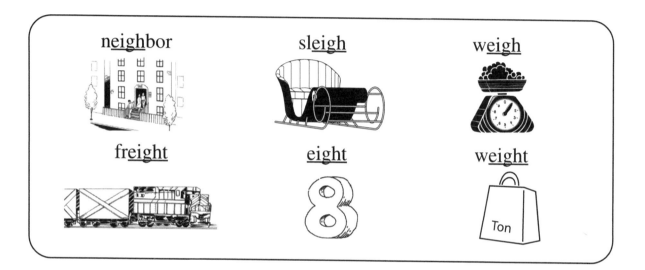

neighbor   sleigh   weigh

freight   eight   weight

Ton

n_____bor   1. Mrs. Ramirez is my _____.

fr_____t   2. That is a _____ train.

_____t   3. That is the number _____.

w_____   4. The lady will _____ the tomatoes.

w_____t   5. His _____ shows on the scale.

TO THE TEACHER: Discuss the meaning of the word <u>neighbor</u>. Discuss how neighbors help each other. Ask: *Who are your neighbors? How do your neighbors help you?*

• Read the questions first, and then read the passage together.
• Fill in the bubble for each correct answer. Read the poem to a partner.
• Then ask your partner to draw a picture to illustrate the poem. Switch roles.

My Family's Neighbors

My family has neighbors
to the left and to the right.

These neighbors help my family
during the day and at night.

The lovely Lee family is our neighbor to the right.
They turn on the light when we're not home at night.

The great Garcia family is our neighbor to the left.
They water our flowers during the day when we go away.

My family has neighbors to the left and to the right.
These neighbors help my family during the day and at night.

1. My family's neighbors are -
   ○ the Ramirez family and the Lee family.
   ○ the Lee family and the Garcia family.
   ○ the Jones family and the Garcia family.
   ○ the Lee family and the Carlo family.

2. Which of these pairs of words from the poem rhyme?
   ○ right, left
   ○ right, family
   ○ away, night
   ○ night, right

3. Which of these lines from the poem have words that begin with the same letter?
   ○ My family has neighbors to the left.
   ○ The great Garcia family is our neighbor to the left.
   ○ These neighbors help my family.
   ○ They turn on the light.

4. What is this poem about?
   ○ the Garcia family
   ○ houses in the neighborhood
   ○ silly neighbors
   ○ helpful neighbors

ELD Standard
Identify and produce rhyming words.
ELA Standard
Identify rhyme, rhythm, and alliteration in poetry.

- Write a story about the pictures.
- Use the writing checklist on page 253 to edit your work.
- Read the story to a partner.

1

2

3

They have rakes._____

_____

_____

_____

_____

_____

_____

_____

ELD Standard
Edit writing for basic conventions and make some corrections.
ELA Standard
Move through a logical sequence of events.

TO THE TEACHER: Teach the spelling pattern **_ought** with Spelling Friend Card #53. Blend the initial consonant sounds to the sound-spelling pattern. Discuss the meaning of the words.

• Dictate the words on Spelling Friend Card #53 to a partner. Switch roles.
• Write the missing **_ought** spelling pattern in each word.
• Write the word in the sentence. Read the sentences to a partner.

bought   brought   thought   fought

br_____   1. Mom _____ the groceries home in a shopping bag.

th_____   2. He _____ he knew the answer.

f_____   3. The two boxers _____ in the ring.

b_____   4. Rosa _____ a dress at the mall.

TO THE TEACHER: Pronounce the word **dough** and show the children the dough in the illustration. Now show them the word dough in the story title. Point out that words with the same spelling pattern sometimes are pronounced differently. Compare and contrast the pronunciation of **dough**, **cough**, and **rough**. Now pronounce **dough** with the words on page 118.

• Read the questions, and then read the passage.
• Fill in the bubble for each correct answer.
• Read the passage to a partner.

Bread Dough

Have you ever made anything out of dough? Many foods are made out of dough. This is how you make bread dough:

First, mix yeast with a little water.

Second, add two cups of flour and warm water to the yeast.

Third, add honey and baking soda.

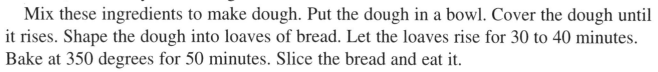

Mix these ingredients to make dough. Put the dough in a bowl. Cover the dough until it rises. Shape the dough into loaves of bread. Let the loaves rise for 30 to 40 minutes. Bake at 350 degrees for 50 minutes. Slice the bread and eat it.

1. What can be made out of dough?
   ○ cars   ○ candy
   ○ bread   ○ paper

2. What do you do first to make bread dough?
   ○ bake the bread
   ○ add honey and baking soda
   ○ mix yeast with a little water
   ○ add flour and water

3. This story was written to tell you –
   ○ where to go to buy bread.
   ○ how to make bread.
   ○ why bread rises.
   ○ what is the best kind of bread.

4. In this story, <u>ingredients</u> means –
   ○ all the things bread is made of.
   ○ the honey.
   ○ the inside of the oven.
   ○ make a loaf.

5. Why is the dough put in a covered bowl?
   ○ to wash   ○ to cut
   ○ to dry out   ○ to rise

6. How many minutes do you bake the bread?
   ○ 50 minutes
   ○ 30 minutes
   ○ 20 minutes
   ○ 10 minutes

ELD Standard
Use the content of the story to draw logical inferences.
ELA Standard
Use knowledge of the author's purpose to comprehend information in a text.

Narrative Writing

- Discuss what is happening in each picture to a partner.
- Finish the story.
- Use the writing checklist on page 253 to edit your work.
- Read the story to a partner.

1   2   3

The man is washing the car with soap._____

_____

_____

_____

_____

_____

_____

_____

ELD Standard
Edit writing for basic conventions and make some corrections.
ELA Standard
Move through a logical sequence of events.

Word Families, Spelling Friend _ick

 TO THE TEACHER: Teach the short ĭ vowel sound-spelling pattern **_ick** with Spelling Friend Card #42. Blend the initial consonant sounds to the sound-spelling pattern. Discuss the meaning of each word in the box.

• Dictate the words on Spelling Friend Card #42 to a partner. Switch roles.
• Draw a picture and write a sentence for each word. Read the sentences to a partner.

| s**ick** | l**ick** | p**ick** | t**ick** | N**ick** | w**ick** | st**ick** | qu**ick** |

sick

_____

_____

lick

_____

_____

pick

_____

_____

wick

_____

_____

stick

_____

_____

quick

_____

_____

ELD Standard
Recognize and use knowledge of spelling patterns.

ELA Standard Generate the sounds from all the letters and letter patterns, including consonant blends and long- and short-vowel patterns, and blend these sounds into recognizable words.

Creating a Mind Map

 TO THE TEACHER: Discuss the community workers that families depend on. Create a mind map together with students.

• Write the names of the professionals who we depend on to get food and clothing.

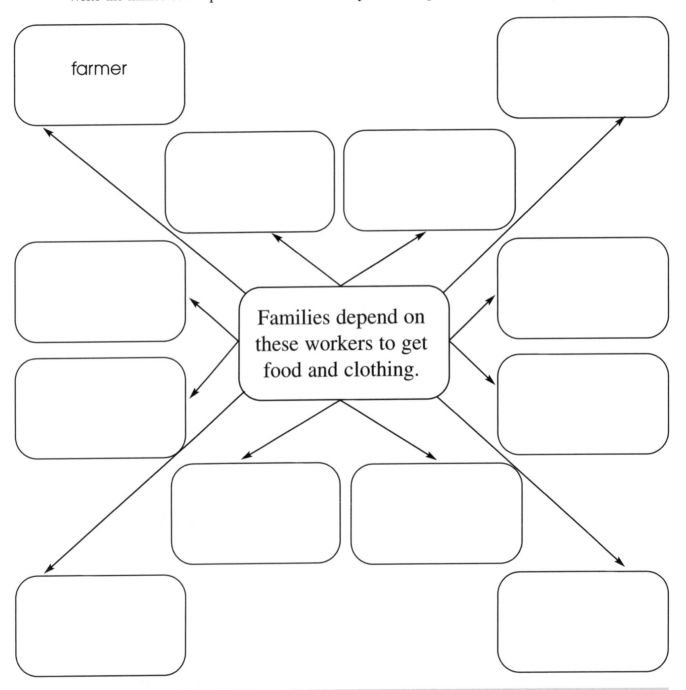

farmer

Families depend on these workers to get food and clothing.

ELD Standard
Apply knowledge of content-related vocabulary to discussions and reading.
ELA Standard
Group related ideas together.

- Read the story.
- Create a story map with a partner.
- Retell the story to a partner.

The Little Red Hen

The little red hen lived on a farm. The little red hen wanted to make some bread.

"Who will help me make some bread?" asked the little red hen.

"Not I," said the goose. "I'm too busy swimming."

"Not I," said the pig. "I'm too busy eating."

"Not I," said the dog. "I'm too busy sleeping."

"Okay," said the little red hen, "I'll make the bread myself."

The little red hen made the bread.

"Who will help me eat the bread?" asked the little red hen.

"I will," said the goose.

"I will," said the pig.

"I will," said the dog.

"No," said the little red hen. "No one wanted to help me make the bread. I made the bread myself. I am going to eat it all myself."

The little red hen ate the bread herself.

Characters	Setting	Problem	Solution

ELD Standard
Write simple sentences about events or characters from familiar stories.
ELA Standard
Retell stories including characters, setting, and plot.

TO THE TEACHER: Review the short ĕ vowel sound-spelling patterns **_ed, _en, _et, _ent** with Spelling Friend Cards #31, #32, #33 and #34. Blend the initial consonant sounds to the sound-spelling patterns. Read the words in the box. Discuss the meaning of each word.

- Dictate the words on Spelling Friend Cards #31, #32, #33 and #34 to a partner. Switch roles.
- Write the correct word in each sentence. Read the sentences to a partner.

b<u>ed</u>   **r<u>ed</u>**   **t<u>en</u>**   **p<u>en</u>**   **s<u>et</u>**   **w<u>et</u>**   **d<u>ent</u>**   **s<u>ent</u>**

1. I have _____ fingers on my hands.

2. Roberto _____ the table for dinner.

3. The rain made the car _____.

4. The apple is _____.

5. The boy is going to sleep in his new _____.

6. The car had a _____ on its front fender.

7. Kim _____ a letter to her friend in Texas.

8. Mom is going to write a letter with the blue _____.

ELD Standard
Read common word families.
ELA Standard Recognize and use knowledge of spelling patterns when reading. Spell basic short-vowel, long-vowel, r-controlled, and consonant-blend patterns correctly.

TO THE TEACHER: Talk about different professions. Ask students if they know of a person who works at night.

- Dictate the questions first, and then read the passage together.
- Fill in the bubble for each correct answer.
- Read the passage to a partner. Then ask your partner to write a summary of the passage. Switch roles.

Night Workers

Turn on the light.
Night workers print the newspaper at night.
That's what they do to get the morning newspaper to you.

Turn on the light.
Night workers bake bread at the bakery at night.
That's what they do to get fresh bread to you in the morning.

Turn on the light.
Night workers put out fires at night.
That's what firefighters do to keep the neighborhood
safe for me and you.

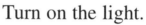

1. Which of these pairs of words from the poem rhyme?
   - ○ right, the
   - ○ fresh, you
   - ○ light, night
   - ○ night, to

2. Which of these lines from the poem have words that begin with the same sound?
   - ○ That's what they do to get fresh bread to you.
   - ○ Night workers put out fires.
   - ○ Night workers bake bread at night.
   - ○ Turn on the light.

3. Which of these lines sounds like it could be part of the poem?
   - ○ This apple is red.
   - ○ Night workers fix roads at night.
   - ○ Where is the bakery?
   - ○ I like to shop at the mall.

4. What is this poem about?
   - ○ day workers
   - ○ night workers
   - ○ firefighters
   - ○ bakers

ELD Standard
Identify and produce rhyming words.
ELA Standard
Identify rhyme, rhythm, and alliteration in poetry.

125

TO THE TEACHER: Discuss the pictures of what this night worker does.

- Write a story about the pictures.
- Use the writing checklist on page 253 to edit your work.
- Read the story to a partner.

1

2

3

The baker is a night worker. _____

_____

_____

_____

_____

_____

_____

ELD Standard
Edit writing for basic conventions and make some corrections.
ELA Standard
Move through a logical sequence of events.

• Read the questions first, and then read the passage.
• Fill in the bubble for each correct answer.
• Read the passage to a partner.
• Retell your partner what you must do to join the Neighborhood Watch Club.

Neighborhood Watch Club

Who can join:

People who live in the Parkwood neighborhood.

People who want to keep their neighborhood Safe.

What to do:

1. First, put a Neighborhood Watch sign in the front window of your house.
2. Ask a friend to walk with you around the neighborhood at least two times a week.
3. Report any crimes in the neighborhood to the police.
4. Clean up the trash and papers in the neighborhood.

5. Fill in the coupon with your name and your neighborhood watch partner's name.
6. Before November 30th, mail your coupon to:

Neighborhood Watch
52 Park Street
Los Angeles, CA

| Name: _____ Date: _____ |
| Partner's Name: _____ |

---

1. To join the Neighborhood Watch Club, you should first –
   ○ phone a friend.
   ○ walk around the neighborhood.
   ○ put a Neighborhood Watch sign in your front window.
   ○ fill out the coupon.

2. To go to the picnic, you must walk around the neighborhood at least –
   ○ two times a week.
   ○ on Fridays.
   ○ on Mondays.
   ○ five times a week.

3. What should you do with the coupon?
   ○ Bring it to the park.
   ○ Mail it.
   ○ Take it to your neighbor.
   ○ Send it to the police.

4. Each coupon asks for -
   ○ your address.
   ○ your name.
   ○ how far you walked.
   ○ your school.

ELD Standard
Narrate and paraphrase events in greater detail using more extended vocabulary.
ELA Standard
Distinguish main ideas and supporting details in expository text.

TO THE TEACHER: Teach the **_ight** spelling pattern with Spelling Friend Card #13. Blend the initial consonant sounds to the sound-spelling pattern. Read the words in the box. Discuss the meaning of each word.

- Dictate the words on Spelling Friend Card #13 to a partner.
- Ask your partner to write the words. Switch roles.
- Write the correct word from the box under each picture. Read the words to a partner.

sight   fight   tight   flight   light   right   night   fright

• Read the questions first, and then read the passage.
• Fill in the bubble for each correct answer.
• Read the passage to a partner.

Firefighter Fox

One day, Firefighter Fox was walking through the neighborhood. He saw some smoke. He looked down the street to see where the smoke was coming from. He heard someone call, "Help, help." Firefighter Fox started running. He saw a small house on fire. It was Rabbit's house!

"Oh, I'm so glad you're here, Firefighter Fox," said Rabbit. "I am so frightened. Please help me."

Firefighter Fox quickly got the hose and started spraying the house. He called 911 on his cell phone. Soon, a fire truck arrived. The firefighters helped Firefighter Fox put out the fire.

"Thank you for helping put out the fire, Firefighter Fox," said Rabbit.

1. Where did Firefighter Fox look to see where the smoke was coming from?
   ○ in the park
   ○ down the street
   ○ in the garage
   ○ The story does not say.

2. When Rabbit saw the fire, he felt –
   ○ happy.
   ○ sleepy.
   ○ frightened.
   ○ silly.

3. At the end of the story, Firefighter Fox was a –
   ○ hero.
   ○ cousin.
   ○ boy.
   ○ doctor.

4. What will Rabbit probably do next?
   ○ get angry at Fox
   ○ buy a new coat
   ○ plant a rose bush
   ○ repair the fire damage on his house

ELD Standard
Use the content of the story to draw logical inferences.
ELA Standard
Use knowledge of the author's purpose to comprehend informational text.

TO THE TEACHER: Review the demonstrative pronouns **this** and **these**. **This** refers to one thing; **these** refers to more than one thing.

- Write the word **this** or **these** in each sentence.
- Read your sentences to a partner.

1. _____ is an apple.

2. _____ boys are friends.

3. _____ book is mine.

4. _____ bikes are ours.

5. Do you live in _____ house?

6. Are _____ your marbles?

7. Who is going to sit in _____ chair?

8. Are you going to pick _____ flowers?

9. Which of _____ dresses is yours?

10. Who owns _____ car?

ELD Standard
Use correct parts of speech, including correct subject-verb agreement.
ELA Standard
Identify and use various parts of speech.

TO THE TEACHER: Teach the spelling pattern **_all** with Spelling Friend Card #54. Blend the initial consonant sounds to the sound-spelling pattern. Discuss the meaning of each word on the card and below.

- Dictate the words on the Spelling Friend Card #54 to a partner.
- Ask your partner to write the words. Switch roles.
- Write the correct word under each picture. Use each word in a sentence.
- Read the sentences to a partner.

| b**all** | c**all** | f**all** | m**all** | t**all** | sm**all** |

_____ 1. _____

_____ 2. _____

_____ 3. _____

_____ 4. _____

ELD Standard
Read common word families.
ELA Standard
Recognize and use knowledge of spelling patterns.

TO THE TEACHER: Teach the spelling patterns **_all**, **_ight** and **wor_** with Spelling Friend Cards #54, #13 and #55. Blend the initial consonant sounds to the sound-spelling patterns. Discuss the meaning of the words on the cards and in the box below.

• Dictate the words on the Spelling Friend Cards #13, #54 and #55 to a partner.
• Ask your partner to write the words. Switch roles.
• Write the correct word in each sentence. Read the sentences to a partner.

ball   fall   tall   mall   call

work   word   night   light   fight

1. The basketball player is very _____.

2. Mrs. Jones goes shopping at the _____.

3. The opposite of day is _____.

4. Where does the man with the briefcase _____?

5. The boy is going to _____ his friend.

6. I am going to look up the _____ in the dictionary.

7. Turn off the _____.

• Look at the graph.
• Answer the questions with a partner.

At the Post Office

15	✉		
14	✉		
13	✉		
12	✉		
11	✉		
10	✉	📦	
9	✉	📦	
8	✉	📦	
7	✉	📦	✉
6	✉	📦	✉
5	✉	📦	✉
4	✉	📦	✉
3	✉	📦	✉
2	✉	📦	✉
1	✉	📦	✉
	Letters	Packages	Overnight Letters

1. Did people mail more letters or packages? _____

2. How many more packages than overnight letters were mailed? _____

3. How many letters and packages were mailed all together? _____

4. Add up the total number of overnight letters and packages mailed. _____

ELD Standard Read and identify text features such as title, table of contents, chapter headings diagrams, charts, glossaries, and indexes in written texts.
ELA Standard
Interpret information from diagrams, charts, and graphs.

TO THE TEACHER: Review the long ā sound-spelling pattern **_ail** with Spelling Friend Card #2. Blend the initial consonant sounds to the sound-spelling pattern. Discuss the meaning of the words on the card and in the box.

- Dictate the words in the box to a partner. Ask your partner to write the words. Switch roles.
- Write the correct word in each sentence. Read the sentences to a partner.

snail   pail   trail   mail

rail   tail   nail   sail

1. Is the carpenter hammering in the _____?

2. Where did he put the mop and _____?

3. The train rides on a _____.

4. That boat has a _____.

5. He saw a _____ in the garden.

6. I'm taking the _____ that leads up the hill.

TO THE TEACHER: Discuss the meaning of the word **communication**.

- Make a mind map with different types of **communication**.
- Write about your favorite type of communication.

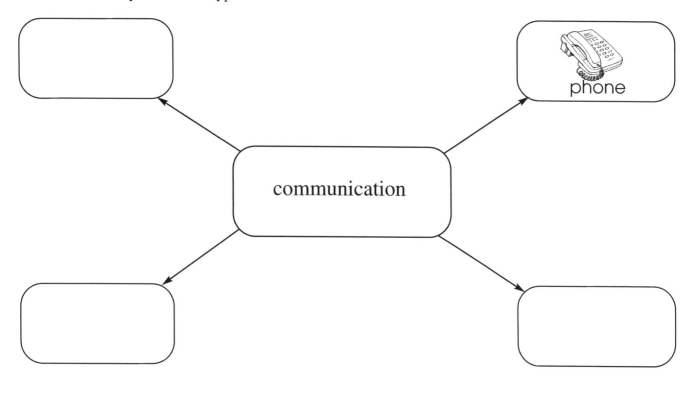

My favorite type of communication is _____

_____

_____

_____

_____

ELD Standard
Demonstrate knowledge of vocabulary.
ELA Standard
Group related words together.

TO THE TEACHER: Teach the spelling pattern **_er** with Spelling Friend Card #56. Blend the initial consonant sounds to the sound-spelling pattern. Discuss the meaning of each word in the box below.

• Dictate the words below to a partner. Switch roles.
• Write the correct word in each riddle.
• Write a sentence for *butter* and *letter* at the bottom of the page.
• Then read the sentences to a partner.

> **butter**   **letter**   **sweater**   **toaster**   **catcher**

1. You put this on bread.

   It is _____.

2. You put this on when you are cold.

   It is a _____.

3. You see him on a baseball field.

   He is a _____.

4. You cook your bread in this.

   It is a _____.

5. You mail this at the post office.

   It is a _____.

butt<u>er</u>   _____

lett<u>er</u>   _____

TO THE TEACHER: Identify <u>nouns</u> and <u>verbs</u>. A <u>noun</u> is the name of a person, place, or thing. A <u>verb</u> is an action word.

- Write <u>**noun**</u> or <u>**verb**</u> under each picture.
- Read the words to a partner.

run

___verb___

Maria

_____

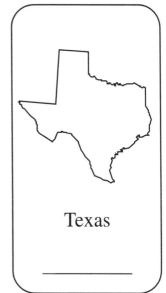

Texas

_____

ride

_____

sit

_____

wagon

_____

Grandma

_____

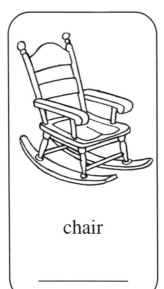

chair

_____

ELD Standard
Use correct parts of speech, including correct subject-verb agreement.
ELA Standard
Identify and correctly use various parts of speech, including nouns and verbs, in writing and speaking.

TO THE TEACHER: Teach the sound-spelling patterns **_ound** and **_ouse** with Spelling Friend Cards #57 and #58. Blend the initial consonant sounds to the sound spelling patterns. Read the words in the box. Discuss the meaning of each word.

• Dictate the words below to a partner. Switch roles.
• Write the correct word in each sentence.
• Write a sentence for the words **shout** and **out** at the bottom of the page. Read the sentences to a partner.

round   hound   mound

pound   mouse   house

1. A dog is sometimes called a _____.

2. Please give me a _____ of potatoes.

3. A circle is _____.

4. A _____ is a small animal.

sh<u>out</u> _____.

<u>out</u> _____.

TO THE TEACHER: Teach the words <u>built</u>, <u>foundation</u>, <u>concrete</u> and <u>wood</u>.

• Read the questions first, and then read the passage.
• Fill in the bubble for each correct answers.
• Read the passage to a partner. Draw a picture of Rabbit's new house. On a separate sheet of paper write a brief story summary.

Rabbit's New House

After the fire, Rabbit decided to rebuild his house. First, he poured the concrete foundation. Second, he built the frame of the house out of wood. Third, he built a roof. Fourth, he put drywall over the wood. Finally, he was ready to paint. Rabbit invited his friends over to help.

1. This story was written to tell you –
   ○ how to pour a foundation.
   ○ why Rabbit needed friends to help him.
   ○ where you can buy wood.
   ○ how Rabbit built a new house.

2. In this story, to <u>rebuild</u> means to –
   ○ repaint.
   ○ build something again.
   ○ make a foundation.
   ○ make smaller.

3. What is another good name for this story?
   ○ Painting with Friends
   ○ Rebuilding a House
   ○ Painting a House
   ○ Running a Race

4. This story is most like a –
   ○ fairy tale.
   ○ true story.
   ○ poem.
   ○ science fiction story.

5. What will probably happen next?
   ○ Rabbit will buy a new car.
   ○ Rabbit's friends will help him paint.
   ○ Rabbit will build another roof.
   ○ Rabbit will plant grass.

Rabbit's New House

ELD Standard
Write a brief story summary.
ELA Standard
Use knowledge of the author's purpose to comprehend information in text.

Identifying Nouns and Verbs

 TO THE TEACHER: Review the definitions of **nouns** and **verbs**.

• Underline the nouns and circle the verbs in each sentence.

• Read the sentences to a partner.

A **noun** is the name of a person, place or thing.

A verb is an action word.

Example: The **girl** (walked) slowly.

1. The firefighter ran.

2. The dog barked.

3. Mike walks quickly.

4. The lady laughs.

5. The baby cries loudly.

6. The man talks a lot.

7. The cat meows.

8. The boy jumped up.

9. The teacher reads.

10. The jet flies quickly.

11. The robot sweeps the floor.

12. The parrot talks.

13. Astronauts exercise daily.

14. Calculators add quickly.

15. The flower blooms.

ELD Standard
Use correct parts of speech, including correct subject-verb agreement.

...us parts of speech, including nouns and verbs, in writing and speaking.

Word Families, Spelling Friend _ill

 TO THE TEACHER: Teach the short ĭ sound-spelling pattern **_ill** with Spelling Friend Card #43. Blend the initial consonant sounds to the sound spelling pattern. Discuss the meaning of the words in the box.

- Dictate the words below to a partner. Switch roles.
- Write the letter pattern **_ill** to make a word. Write the word in the sentence.
- Read the sentences to a partner.

hill   dill   spill   bill

sill   pill   mill   drill

d___   1.   Is that a _____ pickle?

dr___   2.   He uses a _____ to make a hole.

sp___   3.   Did the milk _____?

p___   4.   Where is my vitamin _____?

b___   5.   The bird has a _____.

ELD Standard Generate the sounds from all letters and letter patterns, including consonant blends and long- and short-vowel patterns (i.e., phonograms), and blend these sounds into recognizable words.
ELA Standard Recognize and use knowledge of spelling patterns when reading. Spell basic short-vowel, long-vowel, r-controlled, and consonant-blend patterns correctly.

TO THE TEACHER: Teach the long ē vowel sound-spelling patterns **_eat** and **_eed** with Spelling Friend Cards #7 and #8. Blend the initial consonant sounds to the sound spelling patterns. Read the words in the box below. Discuss the meaning of each word.

- Dictate the words on Spelling Friend Cards #7 and #8 to a partner. Switch roles.
- Write the correct word in each sentence. Read the sentences to a partner.

eat   meat   heat   neat   wheat

weed   feed   need   seed   steed

1.   Is the fan for the _____?

2.   Chicken is one kind of _____.

3.   His homework looks very _____.

4.   That is _____ bread.

5.   Another name for a horse is a _____.

6.   Please plant the _____ in the ground.

7.   Margarita is going to _____ her pet cat.

8.   Lou is going to _____ the hamburger.

9.   Mr. Jones is going to _____ the garden.

10. Do you _____ a new coat?

• Read the questions first, and then read the passage.
• Fill in the bubble for each correct answer.
• Read the passage to a partner. Write a brief summary on a separate sheet of paper.

Grandpa's Chicken Farm

The chickens were walking around pecking at food when Grandpa pulled his truck into the driveway. Grandpa walked over to the chicken coop. He wanted to see how many eggs the chickens had laid. First, he collected the eggs and put them in boxes. Then, Grandpa loaded the boxes of eggs onto the truck. Finally, he took the boxes of eggs to the market.

1. Where does this story take place?
   ○ at the fair
   ○ at the park
   ○ on a farm
   ○ on a boat

2. The boxes show some things that happened in the story.

Grandpa pulled his truck into the driveway.		Grandpa collected the eggs.
1	2	3

Which of these belongs in box 2?
   ○ Grandpa sold the eggs.
   ○ Grandpa walked over to the chicken coop.
   ○ Grandpa went to the market.
   ○ The chickens walked around.

ELD Standard
Write a brief story summary (three to four complete sentences).
ELA Standard
Use knowledge of the author's purpose to comprehend information in text.

TO THE TEACHER: Discuss what is happening in each picture. Teach students how to write a story moving through a logical sequence of events.

- Using the pictures, write a story about how a chick is hatched.
- Use the writing checklist on page 253 to edit your work.
- Read the story to a partner.

1

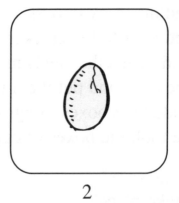

2

3

The chicken is sitting on the eggs._____

_____

_____

_____

_____

_____

_____

ELD Standard
Edit Writing for basic conventions.
ELA Standard
Move through a logical sequence of events.

Identifying Synonyms

• For each vocabulary word, write a synonym, draw a picture, and invent a sentence.
• Read the sentences and show your pictures to a partner.

Vocabulary Word	Synonym	Picture	Sentence
sacks			
stack			
plan			
sound			
pick			

ELD Standard
Explain common synonyms.
ELA Standard
Understand the purposes of various reference materials (e.g., dictionary, thesaurus).

Writing a Friendly Letter

 TO THE TEACHER: Teach the parts of a letter, including **date**, **salutation**, **body**, **closing**, and **signature**.

- Write a letter to a friend about a trip to a farm. Use the pictures to help you.
- Don't forget to write the date at the top of the letter.
- Use the writing checklist on page 253 to edit your work.
- Read the letter to a partner.

1

2

3

Date_____

Dear _____

_____

_____

_____

_____

_____

Your friend,

_____

ELD Standard
Write a friendly letter of a few lines.
ELA Standard
Write a friendly letter complete with date, salutation, body, closing, and signature.

Rhyme, Rhythm and Poetry

Lesson 2.84a

- Read the questions first, and then read the passage.
- Fill in the bubble for each correct answer.
- Read the story to a partner. Ask your partner to retell the story. Switch roles.

Red Cotton Pajamas

I have cotton pajamas.
I wear them to bed.
My cotton pajamas are really red.
My pajamas are made of cotton.
I like my pajamas because they feel so nice.
On my red pajamas are pictures of mice.
There are pictures of tigers and turtles, too.
The tigers look mean. The turtles are green.

1. Which of these pairs of words from the poem rhyme?
   - ○ cotton, mice
   - ○ bed, red
   - ○ mice, bed
   - ○ bed, nice

2. Which of these lines have words that begin with the same sound?
   - ○ I have cotton pajamas.
   - ○ I wear them to bed.
   - ○ My cotton pajamas are really red.
   - ○ The tigers look mean.

3. Which of these lines sounds like it could be part of the poem?
   - ○ My mom slept all night.
   - ○ The mice ran around the bed.
   - ○ Every night I fall asleep in my bed in my pajamas that are red.
   - ○ We grow cotton on our farm.

Identifying Short ŏ and Long ō Vowel Sounds

 TO THE TEACHER: Identify the short ŏ and long ō sound-spelling patterns in each word.

• Write the correct word next to each picture.
• Then write a sentence for each word.
• Read the sentences to a partner.

| n<u>o</u>se | r<u>o</u>se | h<u>o</u>se | ph<u>o</u>ne |
| b<u>ox</u> | f<u>ox</u> | h<u>ot</u> | p<u>ot</u> |

nose

I smell with my nose.

ELD Standard
Distinguish long- and short-vowel sounds in orally stated single syllable words.
ELA Standard Identify short and long vowel sounds. Spell basic short-vowel, long-vowel, r-controlled, and consonant-blend patterns correctly.

Spelling Friend _ead

> **TO THE TEACHER:** Teach the short ĕ vowel spelling pattern **_ead** with Spelling Friend Card #59.
> Blend the initial consonant sounds to the sound spelling pattern. Read the words in the box. Discuss their meanings.

• Dictate the words on Spelling Friend Card #59 to a partner. Switch roles.
• Write the missing letter pattern **_ead** in each word.
• Write the word in the sentence. Read the sentences to a partner.

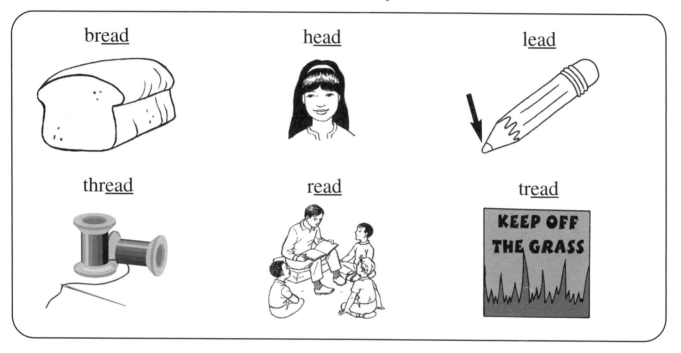

bread   head   lead

thread   read   tread

KEEP OFF THE GRASS

h___   1. He's standing on his _____.

l___   2. The pencil point is _____.

tr___   3. Please _____ lightly on the new grass.

br___   4. Mark made a sandwich with the _____.

thr___   5. Carlos sewed the button on with _____.

r___   6. Who _____ the story to you last night?

TO THE TEACHER: Discuss what is happening in each picture. Teach students how to write a story moving through a logical sequence of events.

- Using the pictures, write a story about how fruit gets to the market.
- Use the writing checklist to edit your work. Read the story to a partner.

1   2   3

He picks the peaches._____

_____

_____

_____

_____

_____

_____

_____

ELD Standard
Edit writing for basic conventions.
ELA Standard
Move through a logical sequence of events.

Word Families, Spelling Friend _unch

Lesson 2.86b

TO THE TEACHER: Review the short ŭ sound-spelling pattern with Spelling Friend Card #37. Blend the initial consonant sounds to the sound spelling pattern. Discuss the meaning of the words in the box.

• Dictate the words in the box to a partner. Switch roles.
• Fill in the vocabulary chart. Read the sentences to a partner.

Vocabulary Word	Synonym	Picture	Sentence
bunch			
lunch			
munch			
punch			

• Read the questions first, and then read the passage together.
• Fill in the bubble for each correct answer.
• Read the passage to a partner.
• Write a brief summary on a separate sheet of paper.

Peaches

These peaches are grown in Chile. Chile is in South America.

It takes eight days for the peaches to travel by ship to California. Before the peaches are ready to be shipped, they must be picked and put in crates. Then, the crates of peaches are loaded onto a truck. The truck takes the crates of peaches to the ship. The crates of peaches are loaded into big containers. The peaches travel in the containers to California.

1. This story was written to –
   ○ tell how peaches are shipped.
   ○ get you to buy peaches.
   ○ tell what Chile looks like.
   ○ give you a recipe.

2. What happens to the peaches first?
   ○ They are crated.
   ○ They are shipped.
   ○ They are picked.
   ○ They are put in big containers.

3. What is the best way to find out more about Chile?
   ○ Have a party.
   ○ Look for a peach pie recipe.
   ○ Read a book about ships.
   ○ Read a book about countries.

4. What will probably happen to the peaches in California?
   ○ They will go back to Chile.
   ○ They will be left on the ship.
   ○ They will be taken to the market.
   ○ They will turn green.

ELD Standard
Write a brief story summary (three to four complete sentences).
ELA Standard
Use knowledge of the author's purpose to comprehend information in text.

Creating a Food Chain

 TO THE TEACHER: Teach the concept of a food chain.

- Create two food chains with a partner. Write a phrase to describe the food chain.
- Ask a partner the question: *What happens in the food chain?*

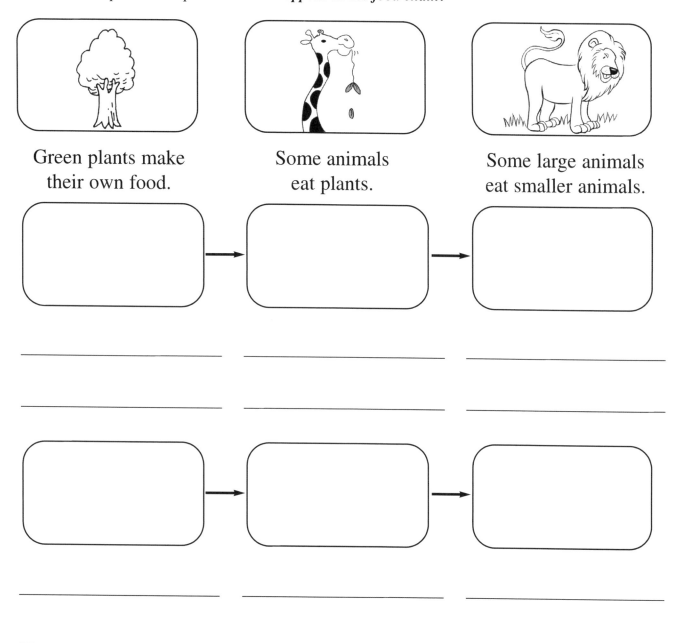

Green plants make
their own food.

Some animals
eat plants.

Some large animals
eat smaller animals.

ELD Standard
Write simple sentences appropriate for language arts and other content areas.
ELA Standard
Interpret information from diagrams, charts, and graphs.

Word Families, Spelling Friend _ew

 TO THE TEACHER: Teach the spelling pattern **_ew** with Spelling Friend Card #60. Blend the initial consonant sounds to the sound spelling patterns. Discuss the meaning of the words in the box.

• Dictate the words in the box to a partner. Ask your partner to write the words. Switch roles.
• Write the correct word in each sentence. Read the sentences to a partner.

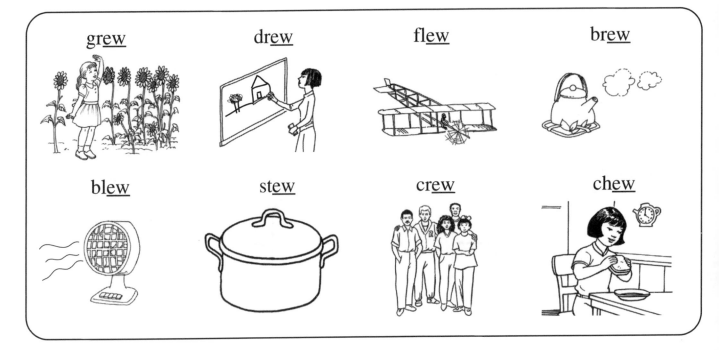

1. The bird _____ into the nest.

2. Are you putting potatoes in the _____?

3. The little girl is trying to _____ her food.

4. She _____ a beautiful picture.

5. The wind _____ through the trees.

6. The flowers _____ after she watered them.

- Read the questions first, and then read the passage together.
- Fill in the bubble for each correct answer.
- Read the passage to a partner. Then ask your partner to retell the story. Switch roles.
- On a separate sheet of paper, draw a picture and write a sentence about the story.

Robbie the Robot

My name is Robbie. I am a robot. Today's a special day. It is the day that I will become part of a family. This is important to me. I don't have a family. My friends are all robots. My friends and I are all made of computer parts. We are programmed to follow directions. My new family will give me directions. I will help my new family cook and clean.

1. This story was written to –
   ○ show how to do something.
   ○ get you to call someone.
   ○ tell about a robot.
   ○ tell about sisters.

2. What is the best way to find out more about robots?
   ○ Read a book about families.
   ○ Make a picture of a family.
   ○ Have lunch in the cafeteria.
   ○ Read a book about robots.

3. What doesn't the robot have?
   ○ a friend
   ○ a computer
   ○ a name
   ○ a family

4. What is the robot programmed to do?
   ○ drink milk
   ○ follow directions
   ○ eat meat
   ○ make friends

ELD Standard
Write captions of words or phrases for drawings related to the story.
ELA Standard
Use knowledge of the author's purpose to comprehend information in text.

Spelling Friends _ome, _oat, _ole

> **TO THE TEACHER:** Teach the long ō vowel sound-spelling patterns **_ome**, **_oat** and **_ole** with Spelling Friend Cards #17, #18 and #19. Blend the initial consonant sounds to the sound spelling patterns. Read the words in the box. Discuss the meaning of each word.

- Dictate the words in the box to a partner. Switch roles.
- Write the correct word in each sentence. Draw a picture for each sentence.
- Read the sentences to a partner.

h**ome**	c**oat**	m**ole**	b**oat**	p**ole**	d**ome**	fl**oat**	h**ole**

The Capitol building has a _____.

My _____ is on Park Street.

A _____ is an animal.

John is going to sail his_____.

The beach ball can _____.

The tetherball is hanging from a _____.

ELD Standard
Recognize and use knowledge of spelling patterns when reading.
ELA Standard
Spell basic short-vowel, long-vowel, r-controlled, and consonant-blend patterns correctly.

156

Making a Mind Map

• Write the words of the things that your family needs.
• Then write the words of the things that your family wants.

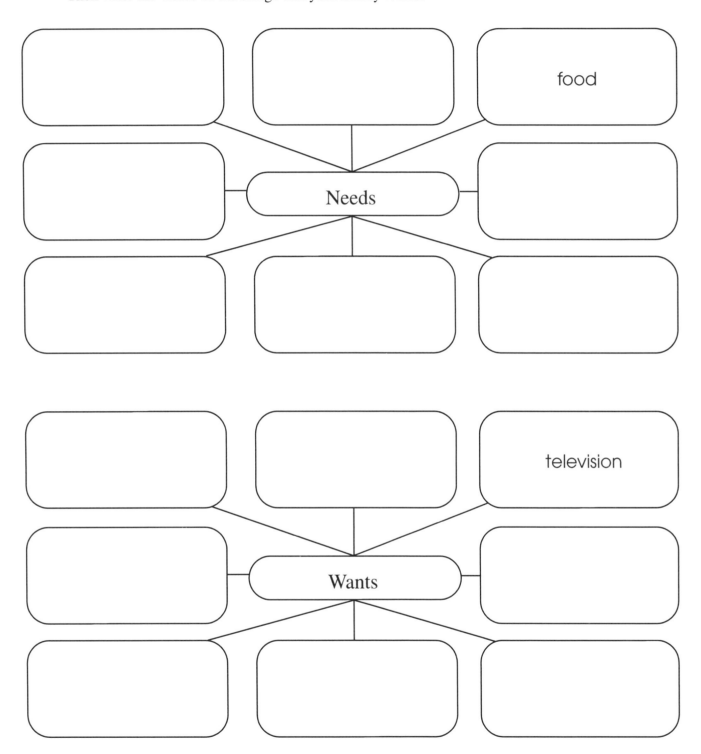

ELD Standard
Apply knowledge of content-related vocabulary to discussions and reading.
ELA Standard
Group related words together.

- Read the story.
- Create a story map with a partner. Draw a picture, and write a sentence for each part.
- Retell the story using the story map.

Turbo Power

The turtle and the rabbit were going to run a race in the park. The rabbit could run very fast. The turtle was worried. How could he win the race?

The turtle talked to his friend, Doc the Scientist. "How can I win the race, Doc?" asked the turtle.

"That's easy," said Doc. "I will attach an engine to you that will give you turbo power."

Doc attached an engine to the turtle. "Thanks, Doc," said the turtle as Doc put the engine on his back. "Now, I can run the race with the rabbit."

The turtle, with his turbo-powered engine, ran the race. The turtle won the race. He ran faster than the rabbit because he had a turbo-powered engine.

Characters	Setting	Problem	Solution

ELD Standard
Write simple sentences about events from simple stories.
ELA Standard
Retell the story, including characters, setting, and plot.

- Read the questions first, and then read the passage.
- Fill in the bubble for each correct answer.
- Read the passage to a partner. Partner retells the story. Switch roles.

Cotton

Cotton is grown from seeds. First, the seeds are planted and watered. The seeds grow into cotton plants. Flowers grow on the plants. The flowers turn into cotton bolls. When the cotton bolls open, it is time to pick the cotton. The cotton is picked by a picking machine. Cotton is made into bales. Cotton bales are taken to the mill to be made into thread and cloth.

1. What do you do first with the cotton seeds?
   - ○ make the seeds into thread
   - ○ plant them
   - ○ pick them
   - ○ make them into bales of cotton

2. Another good name for this story is -
   - ○ Picking Corn.
   - ○ Growing Cotton.
   - ○ Watering Plants.
   - ○ Wheat for Bread.

3. How might you best get the cotton bales to the mill?
   - ○ Take the bales in a wagon.
   - ○ Carry the bales on your back.
   - ○ Take the bales in a truck.
   - ○ Take the bales in a rocket.

4. Which of these sentences would not go with the story?
   - ○ Farmers grow wheat in rows.
   - ○ Cotton is made into clothing.
   - ○ Cotton is grown in rows.
   - ○ Cotton is made into thread.

ELD Standard
Retell stories using expanded vocabulary.
ELA Standard
Use knowledge of the author's purpose to comprehend information in text.

Identifying Consonant Blends

TO THE TEACHER: Review the consonant blends **cl_**, **pl_** and **fl_**. Teach the consonant blends **cr_**, **gr_** and **thr_**. Blend the initial consonant sounds to sound spelling patterns. Then read the list of **cl_**, **pl_**, **fl_**, **cr_**, **gr_**, and **thr_** words in the box. Discuss the meaning of each word.

- Working with a partner, fill in the chart.
- Draw your pictures on a separate sheet of paper.

cl	clown	cloud	clock	click
pl	play	plant	plum	plot
fl	flower	flag	fly	flight
cr	cry	crawl	cream	creek
gr	grapes	grow	green	grab
thr	thread	three	through	

Word	Picture	Sentence
flight		
play		
		I thread the needle.
flag		
grab		
		The baby is going to cry.

ELD Standard
Generate the sounds from all the letters and letter patterns, including consonant blends.
ELA Standard
Spell basic short-vowel, long-vowel, r-controlled, and consonant-blend patterns correctly.

Interpreting Graphs

- Count the number of dresses made at the dress factory each day.
- Fill in the bubble for each correct answer.
- Ask and answer the questions with a partner.

The Dress Factory

The chart shows the number of dresses that were made at the dress factory last week.

Monday	
Tuesday	
Wednesday	
Thursday	
Friday	

1. How many dresses were made on Monday?
   - ○ 20
   - ○ 25
   - ○ 30
   - ○ 50

2. How many more dresses were made on Tuesday than on Thursday?
   - ○ 5
   - ○ 10
   - ○ 15
   - ○ 20

3. The most dresses were made on -
   - ○ Tuesday.
   - ○ Wednesday.
   - ○ Thursday.
   - ○ Friday.

4. How many more dresses were made on Thursday than on Monday?
   - ○ 5
   - ○ 10
   - ○ 15
   - ○ 20

ELD Standard Read and identify text features, such as title, table of contents, chapter headings, diagrams, charts, glossaries, and indexes in written text.
ELA Standard
Interpret information from diagrams, charts, and graphs.

TO THE TEACHER: Teach the sound-spelling patterns **_er** and **_ir** with Spelling Friend Cards #56 and #61. Blend the initial consonant sounds to sound spelling patterns. Discuss the meaning of the words below and on the cards.

• Dictate the words below to a partner. Ask your partner to write the words. Switch roles.

• Write the correct word in each sentence.

• Read the sentences to a partner.

her   letter   partner   mother

stir   bird   third

1. The man is skating with his _____.

2. Please, _____ the soup.

3. The _____ can fly in the sky.

4. Did you mail the _____?

5. Marcos is _____ in line.

6. The baby has a father and a _____.

ELD Standard
Use knowledge of vowel digraphs r-controlled, letter-sound associations to read words.
ELA Standard
Spell basic short -vowel, long-vowel, r-controlled, and consonant blend patterns correctly.

• Identify with a partner the comparatives: **shorter**, **bigger** and **longer**.
• Ask and answer the questions with a partner.

1. Which dog is bigger?
   Write the word <u>bigger</u>
   under the correct picture.

_____   _____

2. Which dress is shorter?
   Write the word <u>shorter</u>
   under the correct picture.

_____   _____

3. Which bench is longer?
   Write the word <u>longer</u>
   under the correct picture.

_____   _____

4. Which hat is bigger?
   Write the word <u>bigger</u>
   under the correct picture.

_____   _____

5. Which pencil is longer?
   Write the word <u>longer</u>
   under the correct picture.

_____   _____

6. Which girl's hair is shorter?
   Write the word <u>shorter</u>
   under the correct picture.

_____   _____

ELD Standard
Use correct parts of speech.
ELA Standard
Identify and correctly use various parts of speech.

Asking Questions Using *How Much*?

 TO THE TEACHER: Discuss the meaning of <u>more</u> and <u>less</u> in relation to money.

• Ask and answer questions using **how much** with a partner: *How much do the _____ cost?*

SHOE STORE PRICES

tennis shoes
$50

boots
$60

high heels
$45

shoes
$35

sandals
$40

ballet slippers
$30

1. How much do the tennis shoes cost? They cost _____.

2. How much do the ballet slippers cost? They cost _____.

3. How much more do the sandals cost than the ballet slippers?

   They cost _____ more.

4. How much less do the sandals cost than the high heels?

   They cost _____ less.

ELD Standard
Ask and answer questions. Apply knowledge of content-related vocabulary to discussions and reading.
ELA Standard
Interpret information from diagrams, charts, and graphs.
164

TO THE TEACHER: Teach the sound-spelling pattern _or_ with Spelling Friend Card #62. Blend the initial consonant sounds to the sound-spelling pattern. Read each word in the box. Discuss the meaning of each word.

• Write the sound-spelling pattern **_or** in each word and in each sentence.
• Read the words and sentences to a partner.

| f**or** | st**ore** | m**ore** | c**ore** | b**ore** | ch**or**e | t**ore** |

f_____   1. This present is _____ you.

st____e   2. Did you buy that at the _____?

m____e   3. We need _____ time.

c____e   4. That is the apple _____.

b____e   5. This is not interesting. It's a _____.

st_____e   6. John buys the video at the video _____.

f_____   7. The postman has a letter _____ you.

st_____e   8. I go shopping for food at the grocery _____.

t_____e   9. The boy _____ up his homework.

ch_____e   10. Taking out the trash is a _____.

TO THE TEACHER: Discuss the meaning of <u>cargo</u>. Discuss the different types of cargo that a ship can carry.

• Circle all the things you can load as cargo onto the ship.

bicycles	bananas	people	dolls
televisions	girls	radios	computers
cars	boys	grandpas	dishes
baseballs	chairs	rugs	tables

ELD Standard
Apply knowledge of content-related vocabulary to discussions and reading.
ELA Standard
Group categories of words.

Word Families Spelling Friend _oo_

Lesson 2.96b

 TO THE TEACHER: Teach the vowel sound-spelling pattern **_oo_** with Spelling Friend Card #63. Blend the consonant sounds to the sound-spelling pattern. Discuss the meaning of each word and the part of speech - **noun** or **verb**.

• Fill in the vocabulary chart. Describe the pictures to a partner.
• Read the sentences to a partner.

Word	Noun or Verb	Picture	Sentence
m<u>oo</u>n			
sp<u>oo</u>n			
ball<u>oo</u>n			
b<u>oo</u>t			
r<u>oo</u>t			

ELD Standard Generate the sounds from all letters and letter patterns, including consonant blends and long- and short-vowel patterns (i.e., phonograms), and blend these sounds into recognizable words. Use correct parts of speech.
ELA Standard Spell basic short-vowel, long-vowel, r-controlled, and consonant-blend patterns correctly. Identify and use various parts of speech, including nouns and verbs, in writing and speaking.

167

- Create a series of rhyming words with a partner.
- Then read the words to a partner.

Example: bat, cat, fat, sat

1. fox _____

2. can _____

3. lot _____

4. run _____

5. it _____

6. set _____

7. pat _____

8. cap _____

9. pen _____

10. top _____

ELD Standard
Create a series of rhyming words, including consonant blends.
ELA Standard
Create a series of rhyming words.

- Read the poem. Underline the rhyming words in the poem.
- Then fill in the bubble for each correct answer.
- Read the poem to a partner.

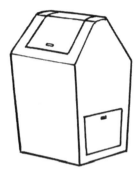

What's a Container?

What's a container?
Is it a box or a fox?

Can you collect cans in a container?
Do they fit inside?
Is a container a place to hide?

Is a lunchbox a container for food?
Is a bottle a container, too?
I can think of lots of containers. Can you?

1. Which of these pairs of words from the poem rhyme?
   - ○ box, fox
   - ○ food, too
   - ○ container, inside
   - ○ hide, food

2. Which of these lines from the poem have words that begin with the same sound?
   - ○ Do they fit inside?
   - ○ Is it a fox or a box?
   - ○ Can you collect cans in a container?
   - ○ Is a bottle a container, too?

3. Which of these lines sounds like it could be part of the poem?
   - ○ A ship can sail.
   - ○ I collect cans.
   - ○ Where is the fox?
   - ○ Is a vase a container, too?

4. Which of these pairs of words from the poem rhyme?
   - ○ inside, fox
   - ○ food, too
   - ○ you, food
   - ○ inside, hide

ELD Standard Read simple poetry and respond to factual comprehension questions. Read short poems and identify the basic elements of rhythm and rhyme.
ELA Standard Identify rhythm, rhyme, and alliteration in poetry.

169

TO THE TEACHER: Discuss the meaning of the word **appliances**. Then teach the meaning of **most** and **least**.

- Read the prices at the appliance store.
- List the items shown from the most to the least expensive with a partner.
- Ask and answer: *Which costs more; the _____ or the _____?*

APPLIANCE STORE

stove $399

refrigerator $438

microwave $258

blender $49

can opener $10

washing machine $595

1. _____

2. _____

3. _____

4. _____

5. _____

6. _____

ELD Standard
Apply knowledge of content-related vocabulary to discussions and reading.
ELA Standard
Interpret information from diagrams, charts, and graphs.

Long ī Vowel Sound, Spelling Friend _y

 TO THE TEACHER: Teach the long ī spelling pattern **_y** with Spelling Friend Card #14. Blend the initial consonant sounds to the sound-spelling pattern. Then discuss the meaning of each word in the box below.

• Dictate the words below to a partner. Ask your partner to write the words. Switch roles.
• Underline the words in the story that end in **_y**.
• Draw a picture to illustrate the story.
• Read the story to a partner.

| by | cry | dry | try | shy | my | fly | why | sly |

_____   _____   _____

_____   _____   _____

_____   _____   _____

My Friend Sly

I have a shy friend named Sly. Why is he shy? I think he's shy because he just moved to our school. Sly sits by me. I try to be his friend. I try to help him with math. When the teacher asks Sly for an answer, he starts to cry. I don't know why. Sly told me he wished he could fly. He wished he could fly back to his old school. I told Sly I want him to be my friend. I told Sly not to cry. I told Sly to keep his eyes dry. I wish I knew why Sly was so shy.

ELD Standard Generate the sounds from all letters and letter patterns, including consonant blends and long- and short-vowel patterns (i.e., phonograms), and blend these sounds into recognizable words.
ELA Standard Recognize and use knowledge of spelling patterns when reading. Spell basic short-vowel, long-vowel, r-controlled, and consonant-blend patterns correctly.

• Read the questions first, and then read the passage.

• Fill in the bubble for each correct answer.

• Read the passage to a partner. Then ask your partner to retell the story. Switch roles.

Toy Store

Miguel and Maria are at the toy store in the mall. They are looking at all the toys. Maria looks at the dolls first. Maria likes the dolls that can talk. She also likes the stuffed teddy bears. Miguel likes the action figures. He likes the race cars and trains, too. Both Miguel and Maria like the computer games.

1. Another good name for the story is -
   ○ A Visit to the Toy Store.
   ○ The Big Train.
   ○ A Computer Game.
   ○ Maria Likes Dolls.

2. What does Maria look at first?
   ○ teddy bears
   ○ trains
   ○ dolls
   ○ cars

3. Which of these sentences would <u>not</u> go with the story?
   ○ Maria likes the pretty dolls.
   ○ Miguel likes the toy trains.
   ○ Maria likes beach balls.
   ○ Miguel and Maria buy a hot dog.

4. What do both Miguel and Maria like?
   ○ trains
   ○ dolls
   ○ cars
   ○ computer games

ELD Standard
Retell stories using expanded vocabulary.
ELA Standard
Use knowledge of the author's purpose to comprehend information in text.

TO THE TEACHER: Teach the spelling pattern **_oy** with Spelling Friend Card #64. Blend the initial consonant sounds to the sound-spelling pattern. Discuss the meaning of the word in each box.

- Dictate the words below to a partner. Switch roles.
- Write a sentence for each word. Read the sentences to a partner.

b<u>oy</u>

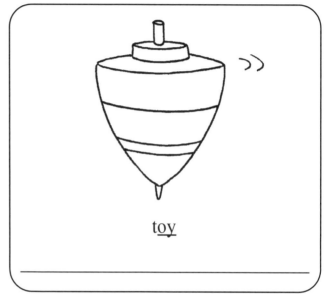

t<u>oy</u>

j<u>oy</u>

R<u>oy</u>

ELD Standard Generate the sounds from all letters and letter patterns, including consonant blends and long- and short-vowel patterns (i.e., phonograms), and blend these sounds into recognizable words.

ELA Standard Read most common word families. Spell basic short-vowel, long-vowel, r-controlled, and consonant-blend patterns correctly.

Creating Past Tense Verbs

 TO THE TEACHER: Review **past tense verbs**. Discuss adding _ed to create the past tense.

• Ask and answer questions with a partner.
• Write the correct past tense verb in each sentence. Read the sentences to a partner.

TODAY	YESTERDAY
help	helped
walk	walked
talk	talked
trade	traded
play	played
ask	asked
wash	washed
watch	watched

1. What did you do yesterday?   I _____ my mom clean the house.

2. What did you do yesterday?   I _____ on the phone.

3. What did you do yesterday?   I _____ my ball for a bat.

4. What did she do yesterday?   She _____ to the library.

5. What did he do yesterday?   He _____ baseball.

6. What did they do yesterday?   They _____ their mother for some money.

7. What did they do yesterday?   They _____ the car.

8. What did they do yesterday?   They _____ television.

ELD Standard
Read inflectional forms (e.g., -s, -ed, -ing) and root words.
ELA Standard
Know the meaning of simple prefixes and suffixes.

• Read the questions first, and then read the passage.
• Fill in the bubble for each correct answer.
• Then, ask and answer the questions with a partner.
• Next, read Angela's chores to a partner.
• Finally, tell a partner what would happen if Angela didn't take out the trash or water the plants.

Angela's Chores

Monday: Take out the trash.
Tuesday: Water the plants.
Wednesday: Sweep the kitchen.
Thursday: Sweep the porch.
Friday: Rake the leaves.
Saturday: Wash the car.
Sunday: Have fun.

1. What does Angela do on Tuesday?
   ○ sweep the porch
   ○ take out the trash
   ○ water the plants
   ○ have fun

2. Which day does Angela have fun?
   ○ Tuesday
   ○ Wednesday
   ○ Saturday
   ○ Sunday

3. How many days does Angela have sweeping to do?
   ○ one
   ○ two
   ○ three
   ○ four

4. What is this passage about?
   ○ taking out the trash
   ○ the broom Angela uses
   ○ the work Angela does everyday
   ○ a clean porch

ELD Standard Read and orally respond to stories and texts by answering factual comprehension questions about cause-and-effect relationships.
ELA Standard Distinguish the main idea and supporting details in expository text.

TO THE TEACHER: Discuss the words <u>community</u>, <u>events</u>, <u>potluck</u>, <u>concert</u>.

• Read the questions first, and then read the passage.
• Fill in the bubble for each correct answer.
• Ask and answer the questions with a partner.

Community Event Calendar	
Day	**Event**
Monday	Book Fair
Tuesday	Car Wash
Wednesday	Baseball Game
Thursday	Potluck Dinner
Friday	Art Show
Saturday	Farmers' Market
Sunday	Music Concert

1. What happens in the community on Wednesday?
   ○ book fair
   ○ car wash
   ○ baseball game
   ○ art show

2. Which day does the community have a farmers' market?
   ○ Monday
   ○ Wednesday
   ○ Saturday
   ○ Sunday

3. How many days does the community have a car wash?
   ○ one
   ○ two
   ○ three
   ○ four

4. What would happen to the farmers' ripe tomatoes if there were no farmers' market?
   ○ They would grow leaves.
   ○ They would spoil.
   ○ They would turn green.
   ○ They would get hard.

ELD Standard Read and orally respond to stories and texts by answering factual comprehension questions about cause-and-effect relationships. Read and identify text features such as title, table of contents, chapter headings, diagrams, charts, glossaries, and indexes in written text.
ELA Standard Interpret information from diagrams, charts, and graphs.

Identifying the Meaning of Prefixes

 TO THE TEACHER: Teach the meanings of the prefixes **un__**, **re__**, and **dis__**. Say the words with the prefixes. Then discuss the meaning of the words with the prefixes.

• In the lines below, write the correct word for each definition.

Prefix	Meaning	Prefix with Word
un	not	unclean (not clean)
re	do it again	replay (play again)
dis	the opposite	dislike (opposite of like)

unclean   unhappy   unable   unreal   replay   reread

disappear   retell   rewrite   dislike   disagree

not happy   _____

to play again   _____

opposite of like   _____

to tell again   _____

to read again   _____

not clean   _____

not real   _____

opposite of agree   _____

ELD Standard
Use simple prefixes attached to known vocabulary.
ELA Standard
Know the meaning of simple prefixes.

TO THE TEACHER: Teach the abbreviations for the months of the year.

- Answer each question using the month, then write the month's abbreviation.
- Underline the months and the abbreviations in your answers.
- Ask and answer the questions with a partner.

Months	Abbreviations	Months	Abbreviations
January	Jan.	July	Jul.
February	Feb.	August	Aug.
March	Mar.	September	Sept.
April	Apr.	October	Oct.
May	——	November	Nov.
June	Jun.	December	Dec.

Example: What is the first month of the year?
<u>January</u> is the first month of the year. <u>Jan</u>.

1. What month is your birthday in?

_____   _____

2. What month begins summer?

_____   _____

3. What month is your mother's birthday in?

_____   _____

4. What month do you like best?

_____   _____

ELD Standard
Use capital letters for proper nouns. Recognize common abbreviations.
ELA Standard
Capitalize all proper nouns, months, and days of the week.

• Read the questions first, and then read the passage.
• Fill in the bubble for each correct answer.
• Read the passage to a partner. Then ask your partner to retell the story. Switch roles.

The Saturday Market

Every Saturday, there is a market in the downtown plaza. Everyone comes to sell things outdoors. First, people set up their tables in the plaza. Then they put the things they want to sell on their tables. Some people sell old toys, lamps, and tools. Some people sell books and magazines. Some people sell fresh fruit and vegetables.

1. Which of these sentences would not go with the story?
   ○ The boys play ball at the park.
   ○ Some people sell old clothing.
   ○ People buy and sell things at the Saturday market.
   ○ Some people sell fruit.

2. What is this story about?
   ○ the new school building
   ○ making a cake
   ○ selling and buying at the market
   ○ a Saturday baseball game

3. What would be another good title for this story?
   ○ Baseball Fun
   ○ A Nice Saturday
   ○ Skating Down the Plaza
   ○ Saturdays at the Downtown Market

4. What is the second thing that sellers do to get ready for the Saturday market?
   ○ put things that they want to sell on the table
   ○ eat breakfast
   ○ buy old toys
   ○ set up the table

ELD Standard
Retell a story using expanded vocabulary.
ELA Standard
Use knowledge of the author's purpose to comprehend information in text.

TO THE TEACHER: Teach the **_ow, _own, _ow_** sound-spelling patterns with Spelling Friend Cards #65, #66 and #67. Blend the initial consonant sounds to the sound-spelling patterns. Discuss the meaning of the words in the box below.

• Dictate the words below to a partner. Switch roles.
• Read the sentences to a partner.
• Write the correct word in each sentence.

flower   shower   power   tower

down   town   frown   clown

1. The opposite of _____ is up.

2. The _____ has a smile.

3. I live in a small _____.

4. Smile. Don't _____.

5. I brought my teacher a _____.

6. Everyday he takes a _____.

ELD Standard
Recognize most common English word parts.
ELA Standard
Spell basic short-vowel, long-vowel, r-controlled, and consonant-blend patterns correctly.

TO THE TEACHER: Bring to class pictures of people ice skating.

- Read the poem.
- Fill in the bubble for each correct answer.
- Underline the words that rhyme in the poem.
- Read the poem to a partner.

Skating

In the summer when it's warm,
I like to skate up and down.
I like to skate around the town.

In the winter when it's cold,
I skate at the ice skating rink.
It is really fun, I think.

Ice skating is very nice
except when I fall and slip,
slither and slide on the cold ice.

1. Which of these pairs of words from the poem rhyme?
   - ○ warm, down
   - ○ slip, nice
   - ○ rink, think
   - ○ cold, nice

2. Which of these lines from the poem have words that begin with the same sounds?
   - ○ I like to skate up and down.
   - ○ It is really fun.
   - ○ I slip, slither, and slide.
   - ○ I like to skate around.

3. Which of these lines sounds like it could be part of the poem?
   - ○ The children eat hot dogs.
   - ○ We played a game.
   - ○ Skating is always fun.
   - ○ The boy threw the ball.

4. Another good name for this poem is -
   - ○ Summer and Winter Skating.
   - ○ The Cold Ice.
   - ○ A Baseball Game.
   - ○ Fun in the Sun.

ELD Standard Read simple poetry and respond to factual comprehension questions. Read short poems and identify the basic elements of rhythm and rhyme.
ELA Standard
Identify rhythm, rhyme, and alliteration in poetry.

TO THE TEACHER: Discuss <u>contractions</u> as the **"short way"** of writing two words.

- Write the contraction for the underlined words in each sentence.
- Read the sentences to a partner.

Two Words	Contraction
does not	doesn't
do not	don't
will not	won't
did not	didn't
is not	isn't

1. She does not eat meat. She _____ eat meat.

2. They do not know how to drive. They _____ know how to drive.

3. Maria will not feed the dog. Maria _____ feed the dog.

4. Pao did not go to the park. Pao _____ go to the park.

5. This is not his lunch. This _____ his lunch.

ELD Standard
Recognize contractions.
ELA Standard
Identify and correctly use contractions.

Spelling Friend _ur

 TO THE TEACHER: Teach the spelling pattern **_ur** with Spelling Friend Card #68. Blend the initial consonant sounds to the sound-spelling pattern. Discuss the meaning of each word on the card.

- Dictate the words in the box below to a partner. Switch roles.
- Write the spelling pattern **_ur** to make a word. Then write the word in the sentence.
- Read the sentences to a partner.

| b<u>ur</u>n | t<u>ur</u>n | ch<u>ur</u>n | f<u>ur</u> |

b_____n   1. The fire is starting to _____.

ch_____n   2. The lady's going to _____ the butter.

t_____n   3. Please _____ around.

f_____   4. The rabbit has white _____.

t_____n   5. Your _____ is next.

b_____n   6. The candles are going to _____.

f_____   7. My cat has gray _____.

ch_____n   8. My stomach is starting to _____.

b_____n   9. They are going to _____ the wood.

t_____n   10. Please _____ the pancakes over.

TO THE TEACHER: Review writing complete sentences with a noun and a verb.

- Draw three pictures that tell a story.
- Draw the first, the second, and the last thing that happened in the story.
- Now write the story.
- Use the writing checklist on page 253 to edit your work.
- Read the story to a partner.

1   2   3

_____

_____

_____

_____

_____

_____

ELD Standard
Use complete sentences and correct word order.
ELA Standard
Write a brief narrative.

TO THE TEACHER: Identify the characters, plot, and setting.

• Read the questions first, and then read the passage.
• Fill in the bubble for each correct answer.
• Read the passage to a partner. Then ask your partner to retell the story.
• Switch roles.

The Year of the Dragon

Every year, Ling celebrates the Chinese New Year with her family. This is the Year of the Dragon. Ling and her family will go to San Francisco to celebrate the new year. First, they will watch the dragon slither down the street in the New Year's parade. Then, they will eat dinner at a Chinese restaurant. Finally, the family will give out money in red envelopes to all the children.

1. Which of these sentences would <u>not</u> go with the story?
   ○ Ling's family celebrates the Chinese New Year.
   ○ Ling's parents give out money in red envelopes.
   ○ Ling's family eats in a Chinese restaurant.
   ○ Ling and her brothers play baseball.

2. Why does the family give out red envelopes?
   ○ to celebrate the 4th of July
   ○ to celebrate Valentine's Day
   ○ to celebrate the Chinese New Year
   ○ to send a letter

3. What is the setting of this story?
   ○ a school
   ○ a park
   ○ Los Angeles
   ○ San Francisco

4. How did the dragon go down the street in the parade?
   ○ It slithered.
   ○ It hopped.
   ○ It ice skated.
   ○ It skied.

TO THE TEACHER: Review the parts of a letter, including <u>**date.**</u> <u>**salutation,**</u> <u>**body,**</u> <u>**closing**</u>, and <u>**signature**</u>.

- Describe what is happening in each picture.
- Use the writing checklist to edit your letter.

- Write a letter to a friend.
- Read the letter to a partner.

1   2   3

Date:_____

Dear _____,

_____

_____

_____

_____

_____

_____

                              Your friend,

                              _____.

ELD Standard
Write a friendly letter of a few lines.
ELA Standard
Write a friendly letter complete with date, salutation, body, closing, and signature.

TO THE TEACHER: Teach the spelling pattern **_tion** with Spelling Friend Card #69. Blend the initial consonant sounds to the sound-spelling pattern. Discuss the meaning of each word.

• Dictate the words below to a partner. Switch roles.
• Write the missing spelling pattern **_tion** to make a word.
• Write the word in the sentence. Read the sentences to a partner.

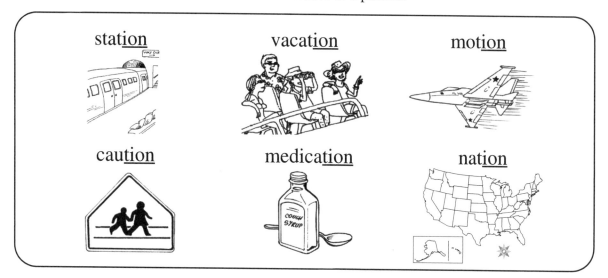

station   vacation   motion

caution   medication   nation

sta_tion_   1. Get the gas for your car at the gas _Station_.

vaca_tion_   2. Where did you go on _vacation_?

mo_tion_   3. The plane was in _motion_.

cau_tion_   4. The yellow light means _caution_.

medica_tion_   5. The doctor, gave Pao _medication_.

na_tion_   6. Our _nation_ is the United States.

> **TO THE TEACHER:** Discuss the meanings of the underlined words. Use context clues to assign a meaning to difficult words.

• Tell a partner the meaning of each underlined word.
• Fill in the bubble for each correct answer.

1. The <u>butcher</u> is going to cut the meat. <u>Butcher</u> means -
   ○ someone who bakes cakes.
   ● someone who cuts meat.
   ○ someone who builds houses.
   ○ someone who delivers milk.

2. The fruit store had only one watermelon, but it had <u>numerous</u> apples. <u>Numerous</u> means -
   ○ funny.
   ○ two.
   ● many.
   ○ noisy.

3. The spice shop had many <u>containers</u> of different spices. The word <u>containers</u> means -
   ○ pencils.
   ○ chairs.
   ○ lamps.
   ● jars.

4. The <u>cashier</u> takes the money at the market. <u>Cashier</u> means -
   ○ someone who carries groceries.
   ○ someone who grows fruit.
   ○ someone who eats cake.
   ● someone who takes cash.

5. Juan's <u>favorite</u> cheese is cheddar cheese. <u>Favorite</u> means -
   ○ found.
   ○ find.
   ● most liked.
   ○ least liked.

6. The dog licked her paws. <u>Paw</u> means -
   ○ tail.   ○ tongue.
   ● foot.   ○ tooth.

ELD Standard
Recognize word meaning.
ELA Standard
Identify the meaning of words in context.

Spelling Friend _ear

 TO THE TEACHER: Teach the spelling pattern **_ear** with Spelling Friend Card #70. Blend the initial consonant sounds to the sound-spelling pattern. Discuss the meaning of the words in the box below.

- Dictate the words to a partner. Switch roles.
- Write the correct word in each sentence.

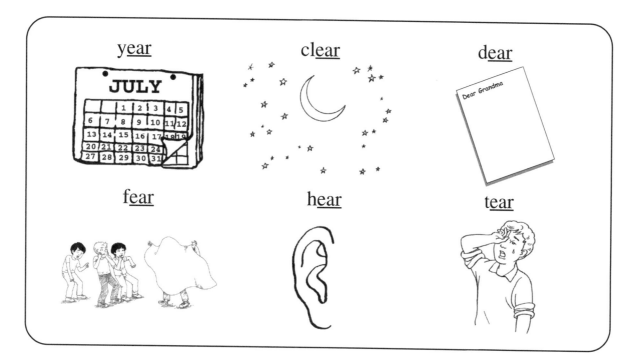

1. The sky had no clouds. It was a _____ night.

2. I started the letter with, "_____ Grandma."

3. He started to cry. I saw a _____.

4. I _____ the radio playing.

5. Don't be afraid of ghosts. Don't have _____.

6. A _____ has 12 months.

TO THE TEACHER: Discuss the Table of Contents below. Discuss the meaning of a chapter. Show children the Table of Contents of a textbook.

• Read the Table of Contents and chapter headings below to a partner.
• Fill in the bubble for each correct answer.

Table of Contents

Chapter	Pages
How to Choose a Game	2 - 8
Checkers	9 - 12
Water Polo	13 - 17
Baseball	18 - 20
Video Games	21 - 23

---

1. Which chapter should you look in to find a game that's played with a bat?
   - ○ Baseball
   - ○ Basketball
   - ○ Water Polo
   - ○ Video Games

2. Which chapter should you look in to find a game that's played in water?
   - ○ Checkers
   - ○ Video Games
   - ○ Water Polo
   - ○ Baseball

3. Which chapter should you look in if you are not sure which game you want to play?
   - ○ Baseball
   - ○ Water Polo
   - ○ Checkers
   - ○ How to Choose a Game

4. Which chapter should you look in to find a board game?
   - ○ Checkers
   - ○ Water Polo
   - ○ Baseball
   - ○ How to Choose a Game

ELD Standard Read and identify text features such as title, table of contents, chapter headings, diagrams, charts, glossaries, and indexes in written texts.
ELA Standard Use titles, tables of contents, and chapter headings to locate information in expository texts.

• Read the **FOR SALE** sign to a partner.
• Ask and answer the questions with a partner.

FOR SALE

Train ticket to Dallas, Texas
Round Trip - $200
Must Sell – Sick, can't go
Please call Jim at
555-2831

1. Who should you contact if you want to buy the train ticket?
   ○ Mary
   ○ the train station
   ○ Jim
   ○ the teacher

2. What will happen if Jim sells the train ticket?
   ○ Jim will go to Texas.
   ○ Jim will get $200.
   ○ Jim will call 555-2831.
   ○ Jim will be a millionaire.

3. Why must Jim sell the train ticket?
   ○ He's going by plane.
   ○ He's tired.
   ○ He's sick.
   ○ He needs the money.

4. Round trip means -
   ○ both ways.
   ○ one way.
   ○ rapid.
   ○ slow travel.

5. Where can you go if you buy the ticket?
   ○ Los Angeles, California
   ○ Freeport, New York
   ○ Dallas, Texas
   ○ Miami, Florida

Identifying Quotations and Ending Punctuation Lesson 2.110

 TO THE TEACHER: Teach the use of quotation marks to indicate someone is talking. Review periods and question marks as end-of-sentence punctuation.

• Write a period or question mark at the end of each sentence.
• Then write the quotation marks in each sentence.

1. Dad said, I'm going to drive to Grandma's house

2. Mom said, I'm going to take the train to Maine

3. Maria asked, How long does the train take to get to Maine

4. Lupita said, I'm going to fly on the plane to Texas

5. Carlos asked, Is it faster to take the train or the plane

6. Nicolas said, I want to visit my friend's farm

7. Mom asked, How many hours does it take to fly from California to New York

8. Mike asked, How long does it take to fly from Los Angeles to San Diego

9. Pao said, I like to drive with Dad

10. Maylee said, I want to fly to Arizona

ELD Standard
Use a period or question mark at the end of the sentence.
ELA Standard
Use quotation marks correctly.

• Read the questions first, and then read the passage.

• Fill in the bubble for each correct answer.

• On a separate sheet of paper, write sentences to tell about your friends that live near and far.

• Read your sentences to a partner.

Friends Near and Far

My friends, Linda and Roberto, live near me in Los Angeles, California. They live on the corner of my street. Everyday, we walk to school together. After school, we play together in the park. We play ball. Sometimes when it rains, we play computer games.

My friends, Shao and Kim, live far away in Virginia Beach, Virginia. We have to take a plane to visit them. The plane trip takes five hours. My family likes to visit these friends during the summer. They live three blocks from the ocean. We walk to the beach. We swim and make sand castles.

I like my friends, Linda and Roberto, who live near me. I also like my friends, Shao and Kim, who live far away. Do you have friends who live near and far away?

1. This story was written to -
   ○ tell about friends who live in San Diego.
   ○ tell about playing in the park.
   ○ tell about friends near and far.
   ○ tell about going to the beach.

2. Which friends live far away?
   ○ Linda and Roberto
   ○ Shao and Kim
   ○ Mike and Beth
   ○ Rebecca and Don

3. What is the best way to find out where Virginia Beach, Virginia is?
   ○ Read a book on cats.
   ○ Take a trip to the airport.
   ○ Find a friend.
   ○ Look on a map.

4. What time of year does the family visit the friends who live far away?
   ○ summer
   ○ winter
   ○ fall
   ○ spring

ELD Standard Read and orally identify relationships between written text and their own experience using simple sentences.
ELA Standard Use knowledge of the author's purpose to comprehend information in text.

- Read the questions first, and then read the passage.
- Fill in the bubble for each correct answer.
- Read the passage to a partner. Then ask your partner to retell the story. Switch roles.

Neighborhoods

There are many different kinds of neighborhoods. A neighborhood is a place where people play and work. There are city neighborhoods and neighborhoods in the suburbs. A suburb is a neighborhood outside the city. Suburbs have big and small houses. Suburbs have movie theaters and parks. Suburbs are nice places to live and work.

1. Which of these sentences would <u>not</u> go with the story?
   - ○ There are many different neighborhoods.
   - ○ The baseball game is in the park.
   - ○ Suburbs have many houses.
   - ○ A suburb is a neighborhood.

2. Another good name for this story is -
   - ○ Driving Home.
   - ○ A Neighborhood in the Suburbs.
   - ○ Dancing Bears.
   - ○ The City Bus.

3. How might you get to a suburb from the city?
   - ○ by rocket ship
   - ○ by car
   - ○ by jet
   - ○ by helicopter

4. A suburb is -
   - ○ a shopping mall.
   - ○ a library.
   - ○ a neighborhood outside the city.
   - ○ a city park.

5. A neighborhood is -
   - ○ a city playground.
   - ○ a tall building.
   - ○ a school playground.
   - ○ a place where people live and work.

ELD Standard
Retell a story using expanded vocabulary.
ELA Standard
Use knowledge of the author's purpose to comprehend information in text.

Adding a Suffix

 TO THE TEACHER: Review the suffix **_ing**. Discuss the rule of dropping the **"e"** before adding **"ing."**

• Write the correct word in each sentence. Read the sentences to a partner.

Root Word	Drop the "e" and add the suffix "ing"
shine	shining
bake	baking
shake	shaking
take	taking
bite	biting
make	making
care	caring
dine	dining

1. shine   shining

The sun is _____.

2. blows   blowing

The wind is _____.

3. bakes   baking

She is _____ the cake.

4. dine   dining

He is _____ at home.

5. makes   making

Mother is _____ dinner.

6. cares   caring

Dad is _____ for the baby.

ELD Standard
Use simple suffixes attached to known vocabulary.
ELA Standard
Know the meaning of simple suffixes.

195

TO THE TEACHER: Teach the words: **dress pattern, material, thread, sewing machine,** and **straight pins.**

• Read the questions first, and then read the passage.
• Fill in the bubble for each correct answer.
• Read the passage to a partner. Ask your partner to retell what is needed to make a dress.

How to Make a Cotton Dress

You will need:
- a dress pattern   • thread
- cotton material   • scissors
- pins   • sewing machine

1. Lay the pattern on the material.
2. Pin the pattern to the material.
3. Cut out the dress pattern with scissors.
4. Sew the pieces of material together on a sewing machine with thread.

1. After you lay the pattern on the material, you should -
   ○ pin the pattern to the material.
   ○ sew the pieces of material together.
   ○ wear the dress.
   ○ cut out the dress pattern with scissors.

2. When you make a dress, the scissors are used to -
   ○ sew the pieces of material together.
   ○ pin the pattern on the material.
   ○ cut out the dress pattern.
   ○ start the sewing machine.

3. What do you do before you sew the pieces of material together?
   ○ wear the dress
   ○ cut out the dress pattern with scissors
   ○ lay the pattern on the material
   ○ pin the pattern on the material

4. This passage is about -
   ○ how to make a cake.
   ○ how to make a birdhouse.
   ○ how to make a painting.
   ○ how to make a dress.

ELD Standard
Describe the main idea and supporting details of a text.
ELA Standard
Distinguish main idea and supporting details in expository text.

TO THE TEACHER: Discuss the meaning of the word <u>ancestors</u>.

- Read the question first, and then read the passage.
- Fill in the bubble for each correct answer.
- Read the passage to a partner. Then ask your partner to retell the story.

My Ancestors

My ancestors came from Mexico. They were farmers in the state of Michoacan. They raised fruit and vegetables.

My grandfather grew up on a farm. As a young boy, he helped his father plant vegetables. My grandfather's favorite crop was tomatoes. My grandfather would help plant the tomato seeds. Then he would water the seeds frequently. As the tomato plants grew, he would weed around them. He tied each tomato plant to a vine. He picked the tomatoes when they turned red. He packed the tomatoes in boxes. He took them to the market to sell them.

My grandfather came to the United States when he was twelve. He often tells us stories about growing up on a farm in Mexico. He tells his class, too. My grandfather is a teacher.

1. This story is about -
   - ○ fun at the park.
   - ○ Grandfather teaching a class.
   - ○ Grandfather's life on a farm in Mexico.
   - ○ selling tomatoes.

2. What would be another good title for this story?
   - ○ Grandfather's Friends
   - ○ How to Grow Oranges
   - ○ Grandfather's Life on the Farm
   - ○ The Big Tomato

3. What did Grandfather do after he planted the tomato seeds?
   - ○ He sold the tomatoes at the market.
   - ○ He watered the tomato plants.
   - ○ He picked the tomatoes.
   - ○ He tied the tomato plants to a vine.

4. What kind of story is this?
   - ○ an animal story
   - ○ a sports story
   - ○ a travel story
   - ○ a family story

5. How does the author feel about his grandfather being a teacher?
   - ○ unhappy   ○ proud
   - ○ angry   ○ tired

ELD Standard
Demonstrate comprehension of a story. Describe the main idea and supporting details of a text.
ELA Standard
Use knowledge of the author's purpose to comprehend information in text. Distinguish main idea and supporting details in expository text.

TO THE TEACHER: Review the spelling pattern _all with Spelling Friend Card #54. Blend the initial consonant sounds to the sound-spelling pattern. Discuss the meaning of the words in the box.

• Dictate the words below to a partner. Switch roles.
• Write the correct word in each question.
• Ask and answer the questions with a partner.

(tall   call   fall   ball   small   mall   stall   wall)

Did she _____?   Did she _____?   Is the mouse _____?

Is the painting on the _____?   Did he play with the _____?

Is the horse in

the _____?

Have you ever gone shopping

at the _____?

- Read the questions first, and then read the poem.
- Fill in the bubble for each correct answer.
- Underline the words that rhyme in the poem.
- Read the poem to a partner.

Train Travel

Long ago, when there weren't any planes,
people traveled on the train.

They traveled on the train.
They traveled whether there was sun or rain.

They traveled to places that were near and far.
They traveled in a passenger car.

They ate delicious dinners in the dining car.
They looked out the window to see the stars.

They slept on the train, too.
They slept in bunk beds with blankets that were red and blue.

Long ago, when there weren't any planes,
people traveled on the train.

1. Which of these pairs of words from the poem rhyme?
   - ○ rain, far
   - ○ train, rain
   - ○ car, rain
   - ○ blue, plane

2. Which of these lines from the poem have words that begin with the same sound?
   - ○ They traveled in a car.
   - ○ They traveled to far away places.
   - ○ They ate delicious dinners.
   - ○ They slept on the train, too.

3. Which of these lines sounds like it could be part of the poem?
   - ○ They traveled in the rain.
   - ○ They rode on a horse.
   - ○ They went shopping.
   - ○ They had fun playing games.

4. What is this poem about?
   - ○ traveling to see Grandfather
   - ○ a long trip
   - ○ travel by car
   - ○ travel by train

ELD Standard Read simple poetry and respond to factual comprehension questions. Read short poems and identify the basic elements of rhythm and rhyme.
ELA Standard Identify rhythm, rhyme, and alliteration in poetry.

TO THE TEACHER: Teach the spelling pattern **_aw** with Spelling Friend Card #71. Blend the initial consonant sounds to the sound-spelling pattern. Discuss the meaning of each word in the box.

• Dictate the words below to a partner. Switch roles.

• Write the missing spelling pattern **_aw** to make a word.

• Write a sentence for each word. Read the sentences to a partner.

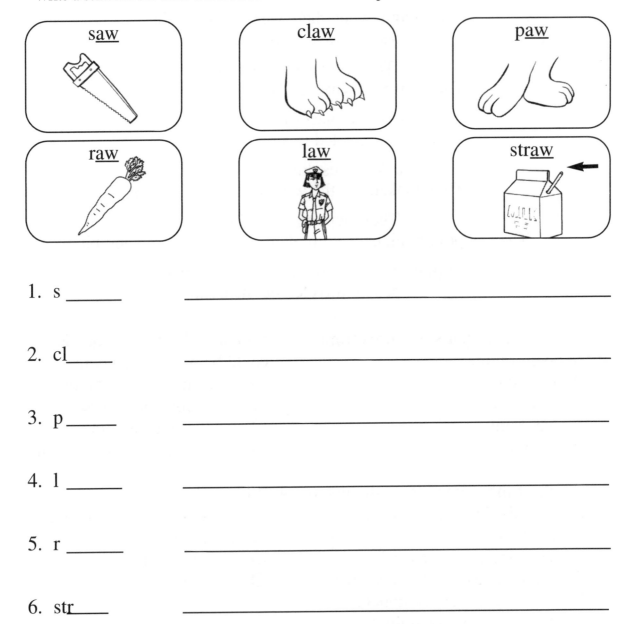

1. s _____   _____

2. cl_____   _____

3. p _____   _____

4. l _____   _____

5. r _____   _____

6. str_____   _____

- Read the questions first, and then read the passage.
- Fill in the bubble for each correct answer.
- Ask and answer the questions with a partner.

Weekly Specials

My grandfather owns a Chinese restaurant. His restaurant is named Lee's Seafood. My grandfather makes a menu of weekly specials. These are special foods that Grandpa cooks each day. This is Grandpa's menu for this week.

MENU OF WEEKLY SPECIALS

Monday:	Steamed Crab
Tuesday:	Broccoli and Beef over Rice
Wednesday:	Chicken Chow Mein
Thursday:	Spicy Shrimp
Friday:	Fish Soup
Saturday:	Roast Duck
Sunday:	No Special

---

1. What is the special on Friday?
   - ○ steamed crab
   - ○ roast duck
   - ○ spicy shrimp
   - ○ fish soup

2. Which day of the week does not have a special?
   - ○ Sunday
   - ○ Monday
   - ○ Tuesday
   - ○ Friday

3. How many days does Grandpa have duck as a special?
   - ○ one
   - ○ two
   - ○ three
   - ○ four

4. This passage is about -
   - ○ eating crab.
   - ○ weekly specials at Lee's Seafood Restaurant.
   - ○ eating fish soup in Hong Kong.
   - ○ Grandpa's favorite food.

ELD Standard Use resources in the text (such as ideas, illustrations, titles, etc.) to draw conclusions and make inferences.
ELA Standard Interpret information from diagrams, charts, and graphs.

TO THE TEACHER: Discuss the word <u>ancestors</u>.

• Read the questions first, and then read the poem.
• Fill in the bubble for each correct answer.
• Underline the words in the poem that rhyme.
• Read the poem to a partner.

Ancestors

Where did your
ancestors come from?

Was it China or Italy?

Did they come to
America on a ship or on
a passenger plane?

Where did your
ancestors come from?

Was it near or far?

Did they come on a train
or in a car?

Where did your
ancestors come from?

Was it Mexico or Spain?

Did they come to
America to live happily?

1. Which of these pairs of words from the poem rhyme?
   ○ happily, from
   ○ from, far
   ○ far, car
   ○ from, Spain

2. Which of these lines from the poem have words that begin with the same sound?
   ○ Was it near or far?
   ○ Did they come on a train?
   ○ Was it China or Italy?
   ○ Did they come to America on a passenger plane?

3. Which of these lines sounds like it could be part of the poem?
   ○ Did your ancestors take a trip on a ship?
   ○ Can you cook rice?
   ○ China is in Asia.
   ○ America has many states.

4. Draw a picture, and write a sentence about where your ancestors came from.

ELD Standard Read simple poetry and respond to factual comprehension questions. Read short poems and identify the basic elements of rhythm and rhyme.
ELA Standard Identify rhythm, rhyme, and alliteration in poetry.

202

Spelling Friends _tion and wa_

 TO THE TEACHER: Review the spelling pattern **_tion** with Spelling Friend Card #69. Teach the spelling pattern **wa_** with Spelling Friend Card #72. Blend the initial consonant sounds to the sound-spelling patterns. Discuss the meaning of each word.

• Dictate the words in the box below to a partner. Switch roles.
• Write the correct word in each question.
• Draw a picture for each question. Ask and answer the questions with a partner.

station   nation   vacation   water   wash   want

Is the United States a _____?

Where is the train _____?

Where do you

_____ your clothes?

Where is the hose to

_____ the plants?

Where are you going on

_____?

What do you _____ for your birthday?

ELD Standard Generate the sounds from all letters and letter patterns, including consonant blends and long- and short-vowel patterns (i.e., phonograms), and blend these sounds into recognizable words.
ELA Standard Recognize and use knowledge of spelling patterns when reading. Spell basic short-vowel, long-vowel, r-controlled, and consonant-blend patterns correctly.

203

Rhythm, Rhyme and Poetry

> **TO THE TEACHER:** Discuss the meaning of a flag. Discuss why the U.S. flag is an important symbol for us as a country.

• Read the poem.
• Ask and answer the questions with a partner.
• Try to memorize the poem.

Our United States Flag

Our fabulous flag is a symbol of the United States,
this is true.
It represents freedom for me and you.

Our flag has stars and stripes, too.
It is red, white and blue.
What does the United States flag mean to you?

1. The United States flag is a -
   ○ part of a ship.
   ○ symbol of freedom.
   ○ symbol for a house.
   ○ symbol for a party.

2. Which of these pairs of words from the poem rhyme?
   ○ flag, you
   ○ true, you
   ○ for, you
   ○ too, stripes

3. Which of these lines from the poem have words that begin with the same letter?
   ○ The flag is a symbol.
   ○ It represents freedom.
   ○ Our flag has stars and stripes.
   ○ What does the United States flag mean to you?

4. Which of these lines sounds as if it could be part of the poem?
   ○ The man rode down the street.
   ○ Is it a sailboat?
   ○ The flag has red and white stripes and stars, too.
   ○ The bird is blue.

5. What is this poem about?
   ○ stars and stripes
   ○ the war
   ○ the United States flag
   ○ red, white and blue dots

ELD Standard Read simple poetry and respond to factual comprehension questions. Read short poems and identify the basic elements of rhythm and rhyme.
ELA Standard Identify rhythm, rhyme, and alliteration in poetry.

Expressing Possession

 TO THE TEACHER: Compare and contrast country flags. Review **'s** to express possession. Note that if a word ends in **"s"**, add the apostrophe only to the end of the word.

- Ask and answer the questions with a partner.
- Write the correct word in each sentence using either 's or s'.

- Example:

Whose flag is this?

This is the United States' flag.

 Brazil

Whose flag is this?

This is _____ flag.

 China

Whose flag is this?

This is _____ flag.

 Egypt

Whose flag is this?

This is _____ flag.

 Italy

Whose flag is this?

This is _____ flag.

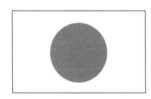 Japan

Whose flag is this?

This is _____ flag.

Honduras

Whose flag is this?

This is _____ flag.

ELD Standard
Ask and answer questions using phrases or simple sentences.
ELA Standard
Identify and correctly use English conventions.

TO THE TEACHER: Teach creating **"fact sentences"** using a lot of detail.

- Design a flag for your family.
- Write about your family's flag.
- Use the writing checklist to edit your work.
- Describe your flag to a partner. For example, describe how the flag looks and feels.
- Read your story to a partner.

My Family's Flag

My family's flag is _____

_____

_____

_____

_____

_____

_____

_____

ELD Standard
Edit writing for basic conventions.
ELA Standard
Revise original draft to improve sequence and provide more descriptive detail.

TO THE TEACHER: Teach the spelling pattern **_alk** with Spelling Friend Card #73. Review the spelling patterns **_eigh** and **_ear** with Spelling Friend Cards #51 and #70. Blend the initial consonant sounds to the sound-spelling patterns. Discuss the meaning of each word in the box below.

- Write the correct word in each sentence.
- Read the sentences to a partner.

w**alk**	t**alk**	ch**alk**	st**alk**
n**eigh**bor	sl**eigh**	w**eigh**	n**eigh**
n**ear**	f**ear**	cl**ear**	h**ear**

1. Write on the board with the _____.

2. You use a scale to see how much you _____.

3. I _____ on the phone.

4. I _____ to school in the morning.

5. My _____ lives next to me.

6. A _____ is used to ride on the snow.

7. Maria likes to _____ the music on the radio.

8. Give me a _____ of celery, please.

ELD Standard Generate the sounds from all letters and letter patterns, including consonant blends and long- and short-vowel patterns (i.e., phonograms), and blend these sounds into recognizable words.
ELA Standard Recognize and use knowledge of spelling patterns when reading.

Identifying Quotations and Ending Punctuation   Lesson 2.120a

 TO THE TEACHER: Review ending punctuation. Discuss the use of periods and question marks. Also, review the use of quotations to indicate what someone is saying.

• Write a period or question mark at the end of each sentence.
• Then put the quotation marks in each sentence.
• Read the sentences to a partner.

He said, "Hi."   He said, "Come."   They said, "This is our house."

1.   He said, This is my neighbor

2.   They asked, Whose coat is this

3.   She asked, What countries are as big as India

4.   He asked, Who are your neighbors

5.   The lady asked, What did you eat for dinner

6.   The clown asked, Do you like my red nose

7.   The teacher said, Take out your spelling books

8.   The policeman said, Don't cross the street when the light is red

9.   He said, My favorite sport is baseball

10. They said, We like to play at the park

ELD Standard
Use correct punctuation.
ELA Standard
Use quotation marks correctly.

Word Families, Spelling Friend _oil

 TO THE TEACHER: Teach the spelling pattern **_oil** with Spelling Friend Card #74. Blend the initial consonant sounds to the sound-spelling pattern; for example, **/b/oil**. Ask: **What's the word?**

- Dictate the words on Spelling Friend Card #74 to a partner. Switch roles.
- Write the correct word in each sentence.
- Read the sentences together and then to a partner.

c<u>oil</u> 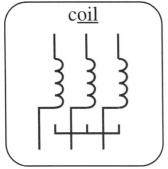	<u>oil</u> 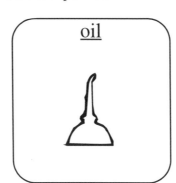	b<u>oil</u> 
br<u>oil</u> 	s<u>oil</u> 	t<u>oil</u> 

1. Put the _____ in the car's engine.

2. Mom is going to _____ the water for the spaghetti.

3. We will _____ the vegetables in the oven.

4. Robert will plant a tree in the _____.

5. A metal _____ is inside the bed.

6. Hard work is called _____.

Spelling Friends _ould and _ous

 TO THE TEACHER: Teach the spelling pattern **_ould** and **_ous** with Spelling Friend Cards #75 and #76. Blend the initial consonant sounds to the sound-spelling patterns. Discuss the meaning of each word.

• Draw a picture for each word.
• Then write each word in a sentence. Use a separate sheet of paper.
• Read the sentences to a partner.

famous	dangerous
_____	_____

glamorous	should
_____	_____

would	could
_____	_____

Table of Contents: Spelling Friends

SOUND-SPELLING PATTERN	SPELLING FRIEND CARD NUMBER	PAGE
Spelling Friend Card Instructions		212
Vowel Sound Long ā	1-4	213
Vowel Sound Long ē	5-10	215-217
Vowel Sound Long ī	11-14	217-219
Vowel Sound Long ō	15-20	219-221
Vowel Sound Long ū	21-22	223
Vowel Sound Short ă	23-27	223-225
Vowel Sound Short ŏ	28-30	225-227
Vowel Sound Short ĕ	31-34	227-229
Vowel Sound Short ŭ	35-38	229-231
Vowel Sound Short ĭ	39-44	231-233
Consonant Digraphs	45-48	235
Other Spelling Patterns	49-76	237-249

Spelling Friend Card Instructions

Introduction:

■ The following pages contain Spelling Friend Cards.

■ These cards will help you to teach students many of the spelling patterns used in the English language.

■ Because each card will be utilized many times, we recommend that you reproduce the cards on tagboard and laminate them.

Suggested Use:

■ Point out the sound-spelling pattern at the top of each card.

■ Show your students the word below the picture.

■ Point out the underlined part of the word.

■ Stress that the underlined part of the word is a pattern.

■ Say the word by blending the initial consonant sound to the sound-spelling pattern.

■ Pronounce each word on the card.

■ Then discuss each word's meaning.

1	Vowel Sound Long ā
Sam	g<u>ame</u>
	bl<u>ame</u>
	f<u>ame</u>
	fr<u>ame</u>
	c<u>ame</u>
Maria	s<u>ame</u>
John	t<u>ame</u>
	fl<u>ame</u>
n<u>ame</u>	

Extended Use:

■ Have students draw a picture for each word written on the Spelling Friend Cards.

■ Then encourage them to write a sentence for each word.

■ Have students choose a partner and have them read their sentences to their partner. They can dictate to each other the words on the Spelling Friend Cards. While one student is dictating the words, the other is writing the words on a separate sheet of paper. Then have students switch roles.

1 Vowel Sound Long ā

Sam

Maria

John

g<u>ame</u>
bl<u>ame</u>
f<u>ame</u>
fr<u>ame</u>
c<u>ame</u>
s<u>ame</u>
t<u>ame</u>
fl<u>ame</u>

n<u>ame</u>

2 Vowel Sound Long ā

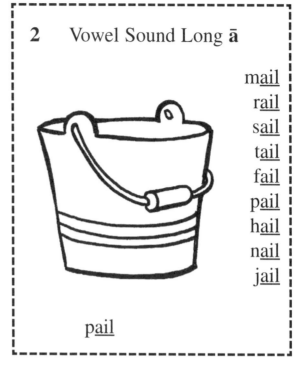

m<u>ail</u>
r<u>ail</u>
s<u>ail</u>
t<u>ail</u>
f<u>ail</u>
p<u>ail</u>
h<u>ail</u>
n<u>ail</u>
j<u>ail</u>

p<u>ail</u>

3 Vowel Sound Long ā

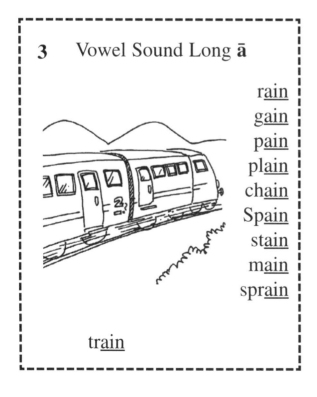

r<u>ain</u>
g<u>ain</u>
p<u>ain</u>
pl<u>ain</u>
ch<u>ain</u>
Sp<u>ain</u>
st<u>ain</u>
m<u>ain</u>
spr<u>ain</u>

tr<u>ain</u>

4 Vowel Sound Long ā

b<u>ay</u>
r<u>ay</u>
h<u>ay</u>
l<u>ay</u>
m<u>ay</u>
p<u>ay</u>
pl<u>ay</u>
cl<u>ay</u>
st<u>ay</u>

d<u>ay</u>

5 Vowel Sound Long ē

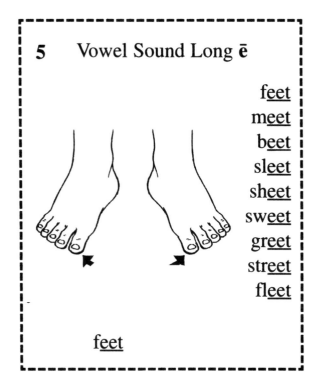

feet
meet
beet
sleet
sheet
sweet
greet
street
fleet

feet

6 Vowel Sound Long ē

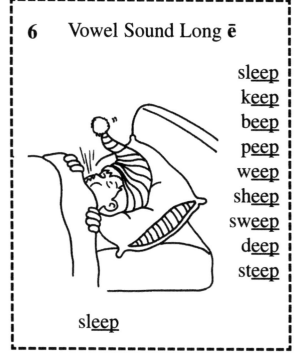

sleep
keep
beep
peep
weep
sheep
sweep
deep
steep

sleep

7 Vowel Sound Long ē

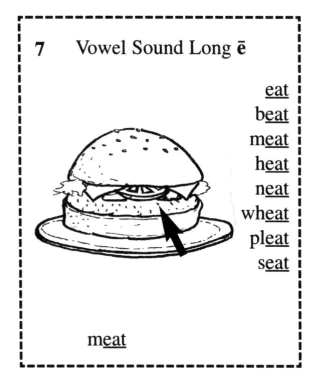

eat
beat
meat
heat
neat
wheat
pleat
seat

meat

8 Vowel Sound Long ē

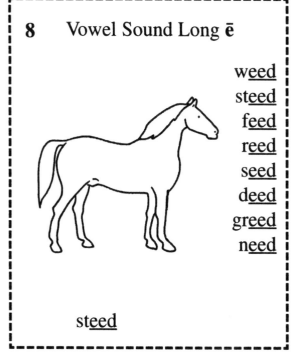

weed
steed
feed
reed
seed
deed
greed
need

steed

（mirrored faded worksheet）

6   Vowel Sound Long ē

sleep
keep
beep
peep
weep
sheep
sweep
deep
steep

sleep

5   Vowel Sound Long ē

feet
meet
beet
sleet
sheet
sweet
greet
sheer
fleet

feet

8   Vowel Sound Long ē

weed
steed
feed
reed
seed
deed
greed
need

steed

7   Vowel Sound Long ē

eat
mean
meat
heat
beat
wheat
pleat
seat

meat

9   Vowel Sound Long ē

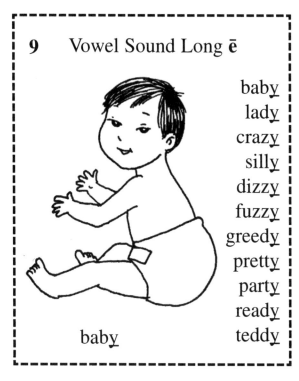

baby
lady
crazy
silly
dizzy
fuzzy
greedy
pretty
party
ready
teddy

baby

10   Vowel Sound Long ē

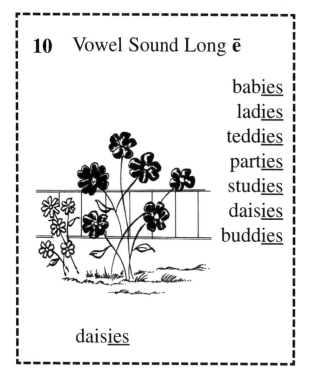

babies
ladies
teddies
parties
studies
daisies
buddies

daisies

11   Vowel Sound Long ī

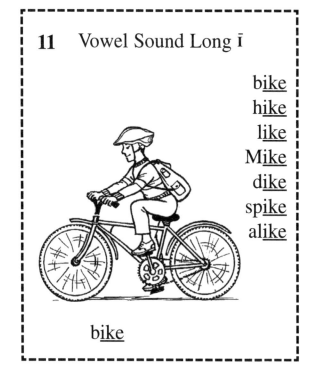

bike
hike
like
Mike
dike
spike
alike

bike

12   Vowel Sound Long ī

hive
five
jive
alive
strive
live
survive

five

9. Vowel Sound Long e

baby
lady
crazy
silly
dizzy
fuzzy
greedy
pretty
party
ready
teddy

baby

10. Vowel Sound Long e

nannies
rallies
teddies
parties
smarties
daisies
buddies

daisy

11. Vowel Sound Long i

bike
hike
like
Mike
dike
spine
dime

bike

12. Vowel Sound Long i

fly
five
fine
dices
solve
lice
survive

five

13 Vowel Sound Long ī

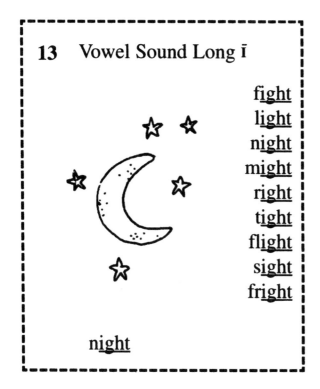

fight
light
night
might
right
tight
flight
sight
fright

night

14 Vowel Sound Long ī

cry
by
dry
try
sky
shy
my
fly
why

cry

15 Vowel Sound Long ō

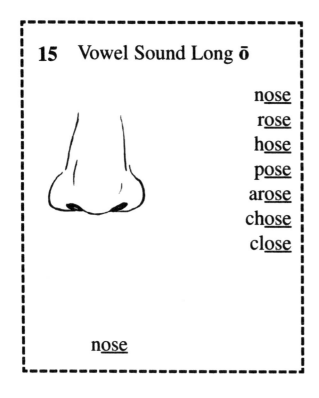

nose
rose
hose
pose
arose
chose
close

nose

16 Vowel Sound Long ō

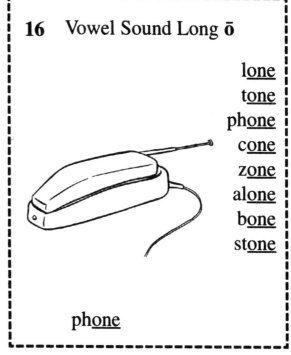

lone
tone
phone
cone
zone
alone
bone
stone

phone

13 Vowel Sound Long i

night
light
might
might
right
tight
fight
sight
right

night

14 Vowel Sound Long i

cry
by
dry
fry
sky
shy
my
fly
why

dry

15 Vowel Sound Long ō

nose
rose
hose
pose
arose
chose
close

nose

16 Vowel Sound Long ō

long
tone
phone
cone
none
alone
bone
stone

phone

17 Vowel Sound Long ō

home
Rome
dome
Nome
chrome

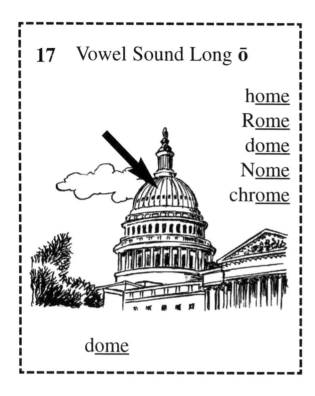

dome

18 Vowel Sound Long ō

coat
boat
moat
float
throat
goat

boat

19 Vowel Sound Long ō

mole
hole
pole
stole
whole
role
sole

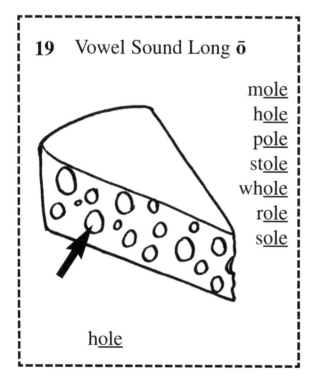

hole

20 Vowel Sound Long ō

low
flow
slow
bow
mow
grow
know
show
throw

throw

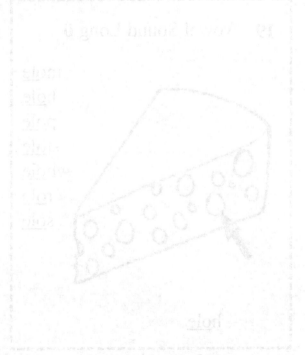

21 Vowel Sound Long **ū**

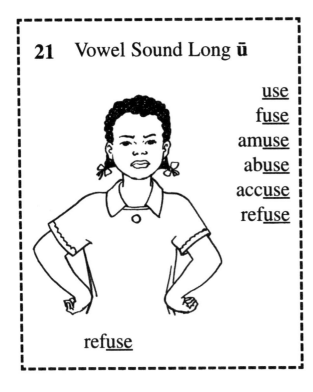

use
fuse
am**use**
ab**use**
acc**use**
ref**use**

ref**use**

22 Vowel Sound Long **ū**

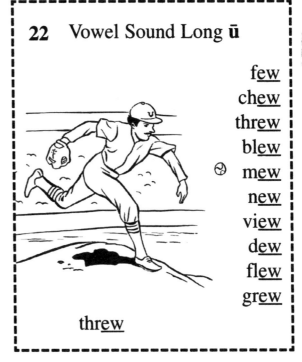

f**ew**
ch**ew**
thr**ew**
bl**ew**
m**ew**
n**ew**
vi**ew**
d**ew**
fl**ew**
gr**ew**

thr**ew**

23 Vowel Sound Short **ă**

b**at**
f**at**
h**at**
m**at**
p**at**
r**at**
c**at**
s**at**
fl**at**

c**at**

24 Vowel Sound Short **ă**

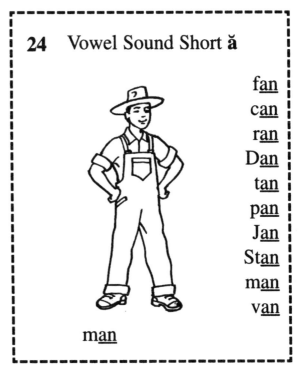

f**an**
c**an**
r**an**
D**an**
t**an**
p**an**
J**an**
St**an**
m**an**
v**an**

m**an**

21 Vowel Sound Long ū

use
fuse
amuse
abuse
accuse
refuse

refuse

22 Vowel Sound Long ū

few
chew
threw
blew
new
new
view
dew
flew
grew

threw

23 Vowel Sound Short ă

bat
fat
hat
mat
pat
rat
cat
sat
hat

cat

24 Vowel Sound Short ă

fan
can
tan
Dan
ran
pan
tan
Stan
man
van

man

25 Vowel Sound Short **ă**

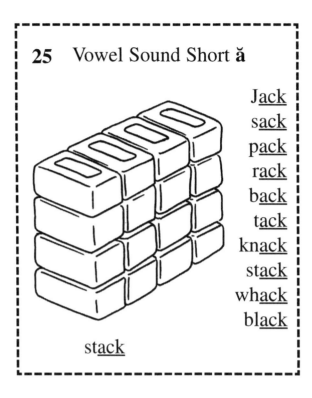

Jack
sack
pack
rack
back
tack
knack
stack
whack
black

stack

26 Vowel Sound Short **ă**

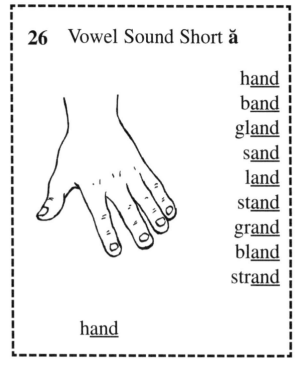

hand
band
gland
sand
land
stand
grand
bland
strand

hand

27 Vowel Sound Short **ă**

ask
task
mask
flask
cask

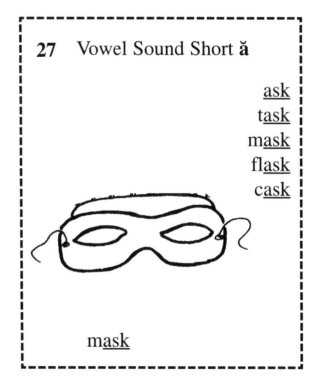

mask

28 Vowel Sound Short **ŏ**

fox
lox
ox
box

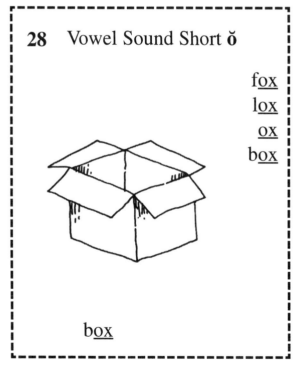

box

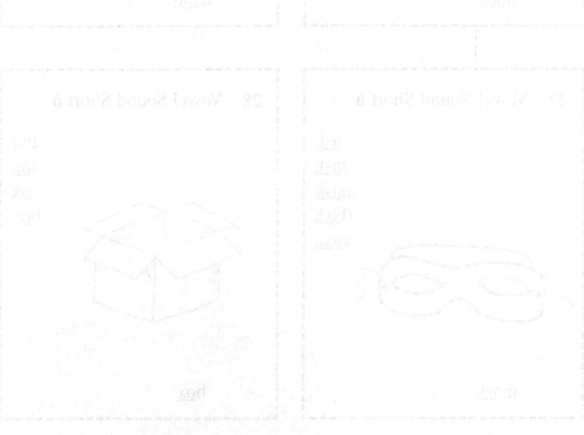

29 Vowel Sound Short ŏ

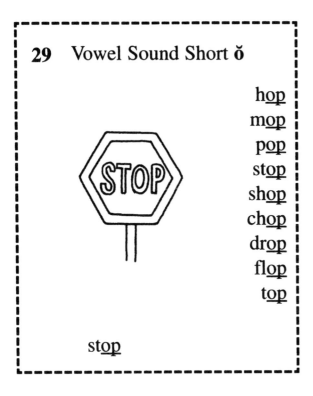

h<u>op</u>
m<u>op</u>
p<u>op</u>
st<u>op</u>
sh<u>op</u>
ch<u>op</u>
dr<u>op</u>
fl<u>op</u>
t<u>op</u>

st<u>op</u>

30 Vowel Sound Short ŏ

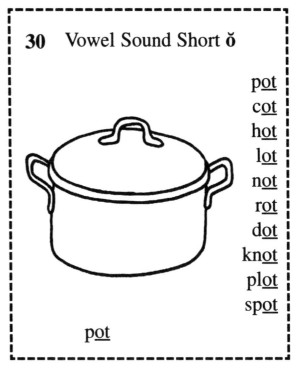

p<u>ot</u>
c<u>ot</u>
h<u>ot</u>
l<u>ot</u>
n<u>ot</u>
r<u>ot</u>
d<u>ot</u>
kn<u>ot</u>
pl<u>ot</u>
sp<u>ot</u>

p<u>ot</u>

31 Vowel Sound Short ĕ

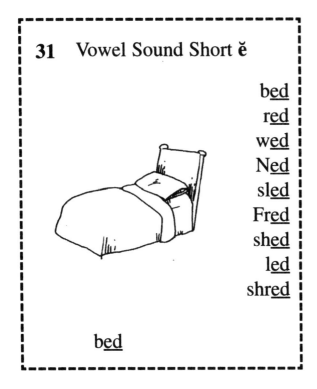

b<u>ed</u>
r<u>ed</u>
w<u>ed</u>
N<u>ed</u>
sl<u>ed</u>
Fr<u>ed</u>
sh<u>ed</u>
l<u>ed</u>
shr<u>ed</u>

b<u>ed</u>

32 Vowel Sound Short ĕ

h<u>en</u>
p<u>en</u>
m<u>en</u>
t<u>en</u>
wh<u>en</u>
th<u>en</u>
B<u>en</u>
d<u>en</u>
K<u>en</u>

h<u>en</u>

29 Vowel Sound Short o

hop
mop
pop
stop
shop
chop
drop
flop
top

stop

30 Vowel Sound Short o

pot
cot
dot
lot
not
rot
tot
knot
plot
shot

pot

31 Vowel Sound Short e

bed
red
wed
Ned
sled
fed
shed
led
bread

bed

32 Vowel Sound Short e

hen
pen
men
ten
when
then
Ken
den
Ken

hen

33 Vowel Sound Short ĕ

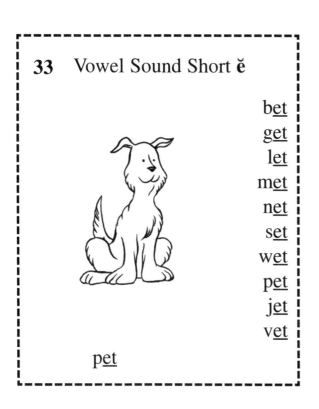

b<u>et</u>
g<u>et</u>
l<u>et</u>
m<u>et</u>
n<u>et</u>
s<u>et</u>
w<u>et</u>
p<u>et</u>
j<u>et</u>
v<u>et</u>

<u>pet</u>

34 Vowel Sound Short ĕ

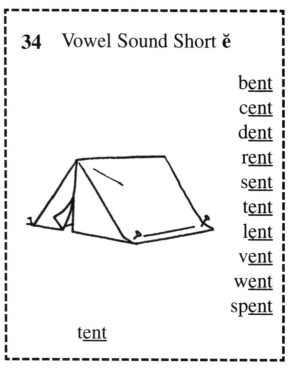

b<u>ent</u>
c<u>ent</u>
d<u>ent</u>
r<u>ent</u>
s<u>ent</u>
t<u>ent</u>
l<u>ent</u>
v<u>ent</u>
w<u>ent</u>
sp<u>ent</u>

<u>tent</u>

35 Vowel Sound Short ŭ

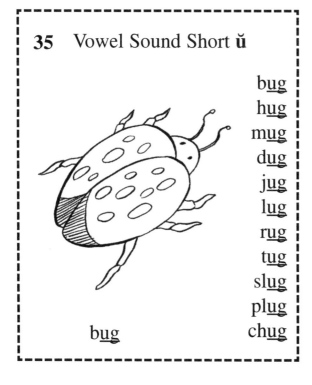

b<u>ug</u>
h<u>ug</u>
m<u>ug</u>
d<u>ug</u>
j<u>ug</u>
l<u>ug</u>
r<u>ug</u>
t<u>ug</u>
sl<u>ug</u>
pl<u>ug</u>
ch<u>ug</u>

<u>bug</u>

36 Vowel Sound Short ŭ

s<u>un</u>
b<u>un</u>
f<u>un</u>
r<u>un</u>
n<u>un</u>
sp<u>un</u>

<u>sun</u>

37 Vowel Sound Short **ŭ**

lunch
bunch
scrunch
munch
hunch
punch
crunch

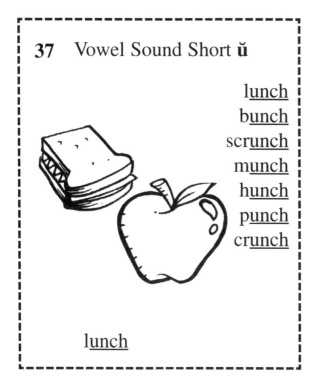

lunch

38 Vowel Sound Short **ŭ**

thumb
crumb
numb
dumb
chum

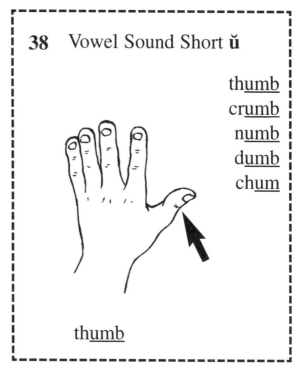

thumb

39 Vowel Sound Short **ĭ**

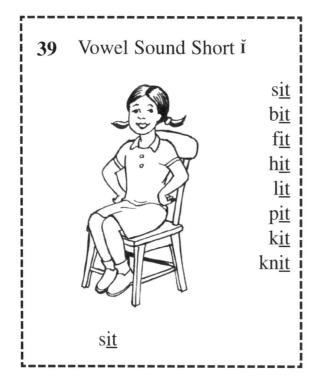

sit
bit
fit
hit
lit
pit
kit
knit

sit

40 Vowel Sound Short **ĭ**

fish
wish
dish
swish
finish
polish
relish
selfish

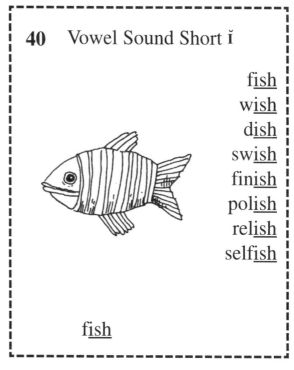

fish

41 Vowel Sound Short ĭ

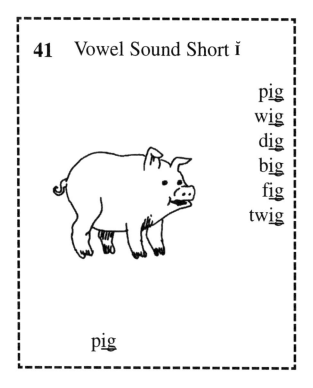

p<u>ig</u>
w<u>ig</u>
d<u>ig</u>
b<u>ig</u>
f<u>ig</u>
tw<u>ig</u>

p<u>ig</u>

42 Vowel Sound Short ĭ

<u>lick</u>
p<u>ick</u>
t<u>ick</u>
N<u>ick</u>
w<u>ick</u>
st<u>ick</u>
qu<u>ick</u>
fl<u>ick</u>
cl<u>ick</u>
k<u>ick</u>

<u>lick</u>

43 Vowel Sound Short ĭ

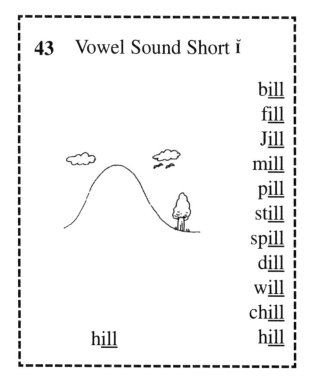

b<u>ill</u>
f<u>ill</u>
J<u>ill</u>
m<u>ill</u>
p<u>ill</u>
st<u>ill</u>
sp<u>ill</u>
d<u>ill</u>
w<u>ill</u>
ch<u>ill</u>
h<u>ill</u>

h<u>ill</u>

44 Vowel Sound Short ĭ

l<u>ive</u>
g<u>ive</u>
r<u>ive</u>r
l<u>ive</u>r
sl<u>ive</u>r

g<u>ive</u>

41 Vowel Sound Short i

pig

43 Vowel Sound Short i

42 Vowel Sound Short i

44 Vowel Sound Short i

five

45 Consonant Digraph
sh

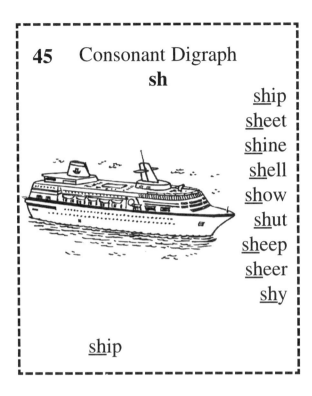

ship
sheet
shine
shell
show
shut
sheep
sheer
shy

ship

46 Consonant Digraph
th

thick
thin
thong
thump
think
threw
thirsty
thirty

threw

47 Consonant Digraph
ch

chip
chunk
chipmunk
churn
chest
church
chief
chime
child
chin

child

48 Consonant Digraph
wh

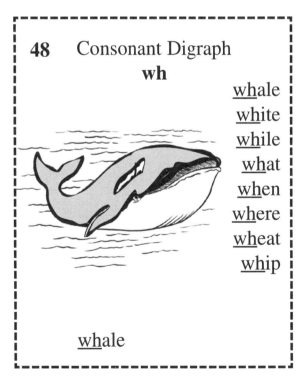

whale
white
while
what
when
where
wheat
whip

whale

49   **_ar**

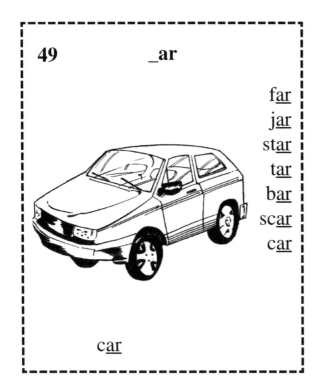

f<u>ar</u>
j<u>ar</u>
st<u>ar</u>
t<u>ar</u>
b<u>ar</u>
sc<u>ar</u>
c<u>ar</u>

c<u>ar</u>

50   **_arm**

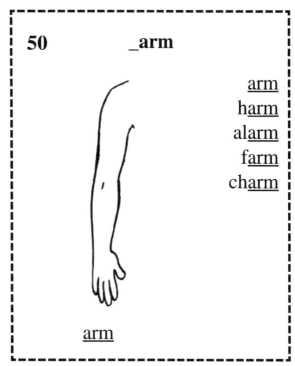

<u>arm</u>
h<u>arm</u>
al<u>arm</u>
f<u>arm</u>
ch<u>arm</u>

<u>arm</u>

51   **_eigh**

w<u>eigh</u>
sl<u>eigh</u>
n<u>eigh</u>bor

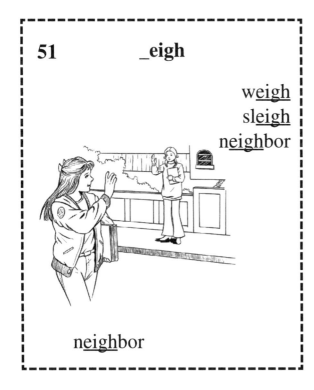

n<u>eigh</u>bor

52   **_eight**

<u>eight</u>
fr<u>eight</u>
w<u>eight</u>

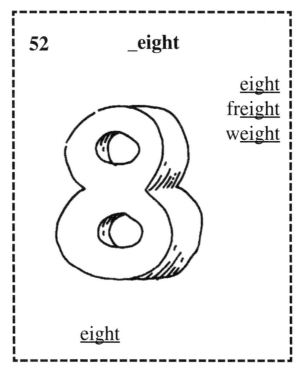

<u>eight</u>

53   _ought

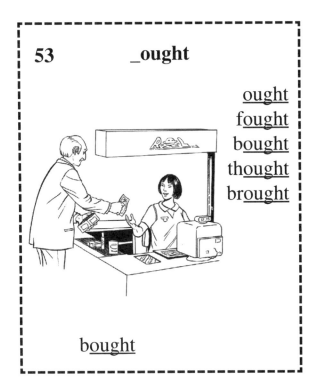

<u>ough</u>t
f<u>ough</u>t
b<u>ough</u>t
th<u>ough</u>t
br<u>ough</u>t

b<u>ough</u>t

54   _all

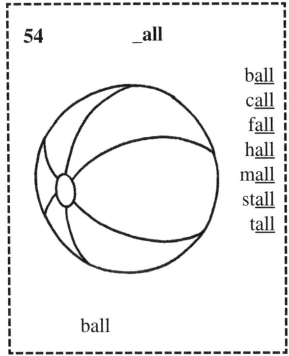

b<u>all</u>
c<u>all</u>
f<u>all</u>
h<u>all</u>
m<u>all</u>
st<u>all</u>
t<u>all</u>

ball

55   wor_

<u>wor</u>k
<u>wor</u>d
<u>wor</u>ld
<u>wor</u>m
<u>wor</u>ry

<u>wor</u>k

56   _er

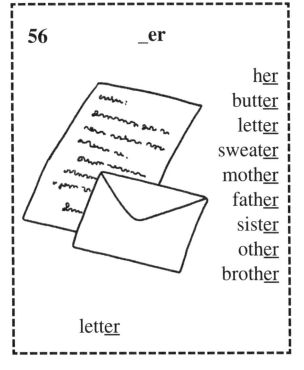

h<u>er</u>
butt<u>er</u>
lett<u>er</u>
sweat<u>er</u>
moth<u>er</u>
fath<u>er</u>
sist<u>er</u>
oth<u>er</u>
broth<u>er</u>

lett<u>er</u>

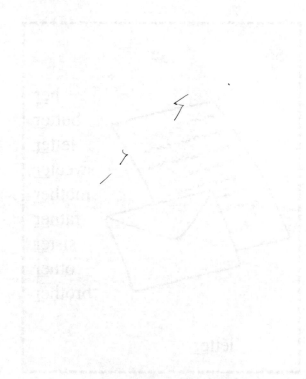

57   _ound

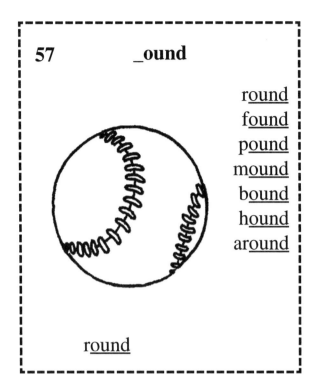

r<u>ound</u>
f<u>ound</u>
p<u>ound</u>
m<u>ound</u>
b<u>ound</u>
h<u>ound</u>
ar<u>ound</u>

r<u>ound</u>

58   _ouse

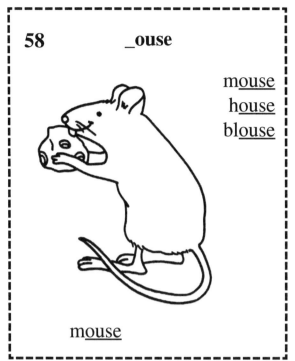

m<u>ouse</u>
h<u>ouse</u>
bl<u>ouse</u>

m<u>ouse</u>

59   _ead

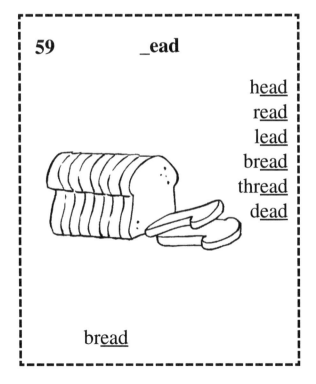

h<u>ead</u>
r<u>ead</u>
l<u>ead</u>
br<u>ead</u>
thr<u>ead</u>
d<u>ead</u>

br<u>ead</u>

60   _ew

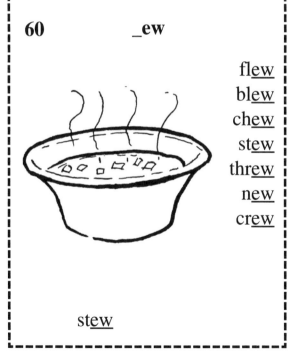

fl<u>ew</u>
bl<u>ew</u>
ch<u>ew</u>
st<u>ew</u>
thr<u>ew</u>
n<u>ew</u>
cr<u>ew</u>

st<u>ew</u>

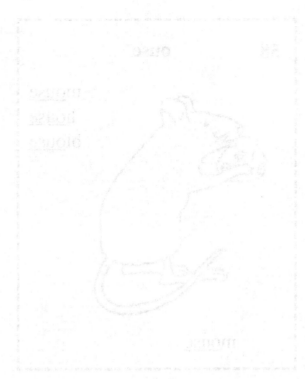

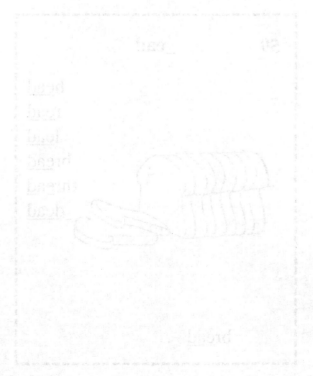

61   _ir_

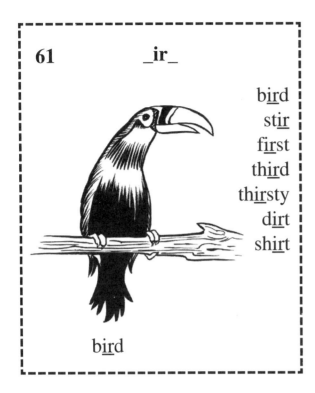

b<u>ir</u>d
st<u>ir</u>
f<u>ir</u>st
th<u>ir</u>d
th<u>ir</u>sty
d<u>ir</u>t
sh<u>ir</u>t

b<u>ir</u>d

62   _or_

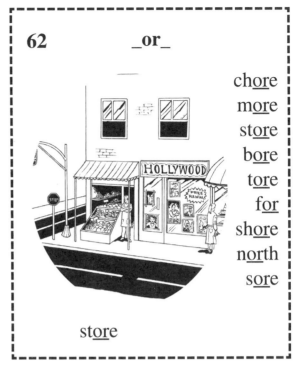

ch<u>or</u>e
m<u>or</u>e
st<u>or</u>e
b<u>or</u>e
t<u>or</u>e
f<u>or</u>
sh<u>or</u>e
n<u>or</u>th
s<u>or</u>e

st<u>or</u>e

63   _oo_

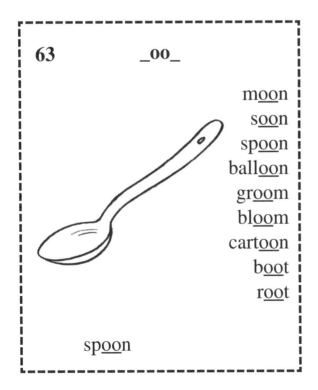

m<u>oo</u>n
s<u>oo</u>n
sp<u>oo</u>n
ball<u>oo</u>n
gr<u>oo</u>m
bl<u>oo</u>m
cart<u>oo</u>n
b<u>oo</u>t
r<u>oo</u>t

sp<u>oo</u>n

64   _oy

b<u>oy</u>
t<u>oy</u>
R<u>oy</u>
enj<u>oy</u>
j<u>oy</u>
l<u>oy</u>al
s<u>oy</u>
v<u>oy</u>age

b<u>oy</u>

65   _ow

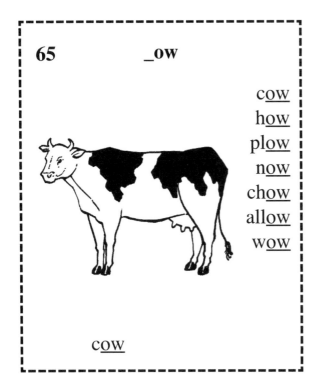

c<u>ow</u>
h<u>ow</u>
pl<u>ow</u>
n<u>ow</u>
ch<u>ow</u>
all<u>ow</u>
w<u>ow</u>

c<u>ow</u>

66   _own

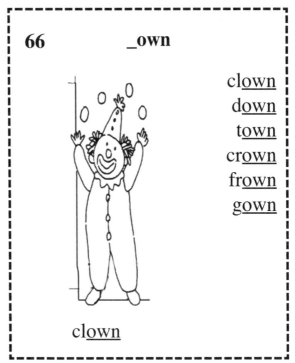

cl<u>own</u>
d<u>own</u>
t<u>own</u>
cr<u>own</u>
fr<u>own</u>
g<u>own</u>

cl<u>own</u>

67   _ow_

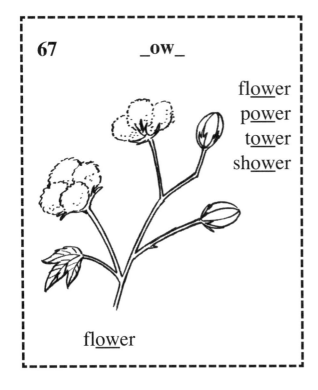

fl<u>ow</u>er
p<u>ow</u>er
t<u>ow</u>er
sh<u>ow</u>er

fl<u>ow</u>er

68   _ur_

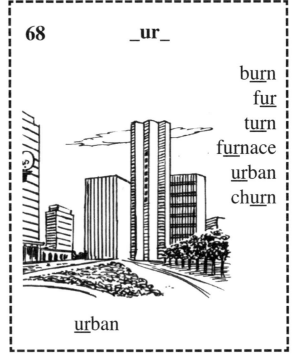

b<u>ur</u>n
f<u>ur</u>
t<u>ur</u>n
f<u>ur</u>nace
<u>ur</u>ban
ch<u>ur</u>n

<u>ur</u>ban

69   **_tion**

sta<u>tion</u>
loca<u>tion</u>
vaca<u>tion</u>
rela<u>tion</u>
na<u>tion</u>
lo<u>tion</u>
mo<u>tion</u>
emo<u>tion</u>

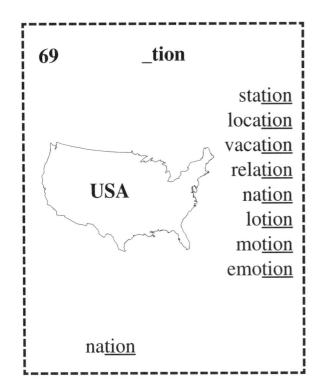

USA

na<u>tion</u>

70   **_ear**

<u>ear</u>
d<u>ear</u>
f<u>ear</u>
y<u>ear</u>
cl<u>ear</u>
app<u>ear</u>
g<u>ear</u>
h<u>ear</u>
n<u>ear</u>

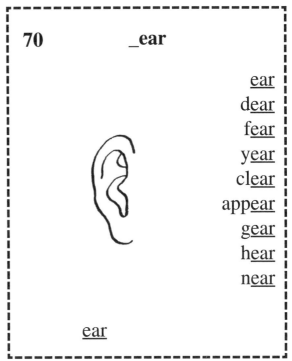

<u>ear</u>

71   **_aw**

s<u>aw</u>
cl<u>aw</u>
fl<u>aw</u>
l<u>aw</u>
r<u>aw</u>
h<u>aw</u>k
str<u>aw</u>
p<u>aw</u>

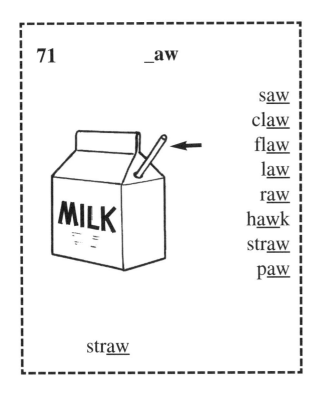

MILK

str<u>aw</u>

72   **wa_**

<u>wa</u>sh
<u>wa</u>nt
<u>wa</u>ter
<u>wa</u>tch
<u>wa</u>ll
<u>wa</u>lk
<u>wa</u>ffle
<u>wa</u>llet

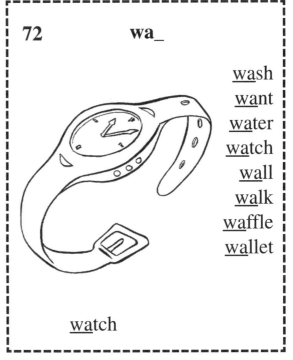

<u>wa</u>tch

247

73   **_alk**

w<u>alk</u>
t<u>alk</u>
ch<u>alk</u>
st<u>alk</u>

t<u>alk</u>

74   **_oil**

<u>oil</u>
c<u>oil</u>
f<u>oil</u>
sp<u>oil</u>
t<u>oil</u>
b<u>oil</u>
br<u>oil</u>

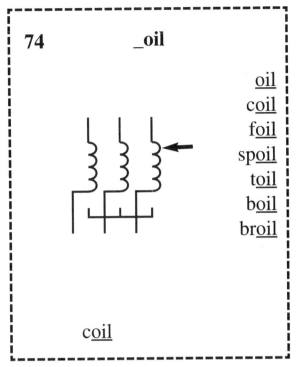

c<u>oil</u>

75   **_ould**

sh<u>ould</u>
w<u>ould</u>
c<u>ould</u>

sh<u>ould</u>

76   **_ous**

fam<u>ous</u>
danger<u>ous</u>
glamor<u>ous</u>

fam<u>ous</u>